# HOLIDAYS AND HOOPLA

## Edward McClenathan

D1372804

# Holidays and Hoopla

*DEDICATION*

*To my children, Scott, Brenda, Todd, and Michael,*
*who taught me more than I taught them.*

# Holidays and Hoopla

# Table of Contents

# Preface

Please consider sharing "Holidays and Hoopla", the nostalgic adventures of Jack Holiday and his friends and foes, with as many interested listeners as you can. You'll warm your own heart as you read aloud of the exploits of youths of a bygone era, intentionally following a familiar school-year calendar.

*(\*Take note, educators and librarians.)*

Those who've lived these experiences will delight in re-living them, while simultaneously introducing the younger set with a look back to a more innocent age of go-carts, tree houses, and the time-honored peaks and valleys of puppy love.

Now gather the troupes and let's join Jack and his friend, Benjie, as they do their best to make the most of a late summer's day. Soon, they'll be returning to school, catching up with their peers, and letting us in on their journey through the everyday trials and joys of growing up in America in the 1960s.

## Chapter I

# Caterpillars, Carriages, and Go-carts

Slouched on his front steps, elbows on knees, chin in his hands, Jack Holiday sat wondering what there was to do. Now and then, he glanced up and down the quiet street. The houses seemed like empty white boxes drowsing in the afternoon sun. The heat of late summer hung heavily in the dark green trees, not a leaf was fluttering. Sitting next to Jack was Benjie, his little pal, who had a stick and was "experimenting" with a fuzzy, brown caterpillar.

"Benjie! Can't you think of anything for us to do?"

Before answering, Benjie watched the caterpillar creep along on the stick like a tightrope walker. "Why don't we get someone to take us swimming?"

"Because the pool's closed!"

"Oh," said Benjie, settling back comfortably on the lawn. He studied the furry caterpillar so closely that it nearly tickled his nose. As the insect reached the top, he turned the twig upside down and the caterpillar began climbing again. Each time the caterpillar reached the top, it stood twisting on its hind legs reaching for somewhere else to climb. After some thought, Benjie looked away from the caterpillar and toward Jack again. "Why don't we make something?" he said.

"Make what?" said Jack. "A clubhouse? We don't have any wood or anyplace to build." His dream, like that of every other kid on the street, was to have a clubhouse where they could hold meetings. Like lightning, his mind could raise up a castle without a single stone for a starter. Too often, his dreams towered beyond his capabilities.

Benjie watched the caterpillar climb again and wondered why it kept trying to get to the top, and where, if anywhere, it had in mind to go.

"Why don't we finish the go-cart? It won't take much to do that," he suggested, his eyes brightening once more.

"Hey, that's a good...no...no, that's no good," said Jack, cradling his chin. "I thought of that last week, remember? It won't take much – only wheels. We don't have any wheels."

"Oh, yeah. Shucks."

The caterpillar, on the bottom for the hundredth time, stopped, reversed, swayed its head from side to side, then humped its way up the stick again. Benjie grinned to himself.

"Isn't it nutty that caterpillars wear fur coats in summer, Jack?"

# Holidays and Hoopla

"Think of something to do, will you?" said Jack, bouncing a teeny pebble off Benjie's head. Jack was naturally blue. Summer vacation was almost over. With school so near, their free time became more and more precious.

"Uh,…why don't we go scare the girls?" said Benjie

"Because we did that yesterday," said Jack, still glued to the steps.

"Oh, yeah," said Benjie, thinking a moment. "But we didn't have a caterpillar to spook 'em with."

Just then, they spied Mary Jane Tompkins coming down the street wheeling her baby sister in a buggy. As always, the boys didn't need plans in order to act. They dashed behind some bushes and waited for Mary Jane to pass. A shriek of surprise from Mary Jane would help liven things up.

After she'd passed, they sneaked up behind her like two cats. Benjie was all set to poke his pet caterpillar at Mary Jane, when she turned and faced them.

What're you trying to scare me with this time, Jack Holiday? You ought to know by now you can't frighten me."

"You would have been scared, if you hadn't seen us coming."

"What are you hiding there, Benjie?" said Mary Jane, rocking the baby carriage.

"I'm not hiding nothing."

"You are so, behind your back."

Benjie saw that any chance of surprise had passed, but he wiggled the caterpillar under her upturned nose just the same.

"You didn't expect me to be frightened at that lepidopterous insect, did you?" she said, pointing her nose in the air.

"Leopard-what?"

"Lepidopterous! Why, when I was in fourth grade, I wrote a two-page report on Lepidopters. The larvae form a cocoon and later emerges as a butterfly and…"

"Okay, smarty-pants," said Jack, turning a deaf ear. To be told anything by Mary Jane was poison, as far as the boys were concerned. "You think you're big because your brain soaks up stuff. Well, so does a sponge."

"And what's wrong with absorbing knowledge, I'd like to know?" said Mary Jane.

"You get a fat head, that's what. You can't fill up a sack without making it bigger, can you?"

"Oh, Jack Holiday, you're terrible!"

While Jack was having words with Mary Jane, Benjie was giving his attention to Mary Jane's little sister, Babsy, who was sitting in the buggy, goo-gooing, drooling, and gumming her rubber teething ring.

"What are you doing, Benjie?" asked Mary Jane.

"Oh, I was just seeing if your baby sister would be scared of the caterpillar," Benjie said, looking up.

"Was she?" Jack asked.

"Naw, she seems more curious than anything," said Benjie, looking back into the buggy. Suddenly, Benjie looked back at Jack and Mary Jane, and turned milk white. "Oh, my gosh!

"What's the matter?"

Benjie raised the naked twig he held in his hand and then, in a choked voice said "I think your baby sister ate my caterpillar!"

Jack and Mary Jane leaped forward and looked at the baby. There she sat, puckering her lips, puffing her cheeks, looking as innocent as a princess, while drool ran down her chin. Mary Jane quickly forced her sister's mouth open.

"Looks empty to me," said Jack.

"Oh, Babsy, you didn't...did you?" said Mary Jane, scrunching up her face.

The baby gazed back happily, smirked a little, and cooed.

"Oh, quick, Jack, quick! Help me turn her upside down," said Mary Jane. "Oh, what will mother say when she hears about this?"

"For gosh sakes, you're not going to tell her, are you?" said Jack.

"Certainly, I'm going to tell her. Who knows what can happen from eating a...," Mary Jane clasped her hand over her mouth, "...a live Lepidoptera."

"Gosh, when you put it that way, it does sound pretty awful. But *you* ought to know. You're the bug expert."

Benjie stood by while Jack and Mary Jane had baby Babsy hung upside down by her heels, trying to shake out the caterpillar. He didn't say a word. He was worried. Or something else was on his mind. Jack and Mary Jane had been too busy putting Babsy topsy-turvy to look elsewhere. In the meantime, Benjie began rummaging through the buggy. Before baby Babsy had been completely disjointed, Benjie announced:

"I've got it! Here it is! I found my caterpillar. It must have dropped off the stick into the buggy."

"Oh, what a relief!" said Mary Jane.

"Yeah, I'm relieved, too." said Benjie.

"That Babsy didn't eat it?!"

"No, that I got my caterpillar back. I thought he was a goner."

Mary Jane returned her baby sister to the buggy and rocked it gently to soothe her jangled nerves. If great inventions start with a sudden burst of inspiration, at this moment, Jack was struck with his. Maybe it was a seed planted earlier that had just sprouted, or an opportunity presenting itself, or maybe it was simply just the way Mary Jane gently rolled the buggy back and forth. Whatever it was, Jack got what he thought was a magnificent idea.

"Come on, Benjie. Let's go do what we were going to do earlier," said Jack.

Benjie, of course, was dumbfounded by this announcement. He didn't know that they had found *anything* to do. A wink from Jack soon set him on the right track. Although Benjie still didn't know the plot, he knew how to play his part like a professional actor.

"Oh, yeah. Let's do it," said Benjie.

Mary Jane fell for it.

"So, what are you going to do, Jack?" she asked.

"Well, I don't really know if we ought to tell you, Mary Jane. We never let any girls in on it before. Have we, Benjie?"

"No, no we haven't. We sure haven't."

"Oh, come on, Jack. Tell me please."

"Well, the only ones in on it have given something towards it. Isn't that so, Benjie?"

"Yeah, that's so," said Benjie.

"Okay for you, Jack," said Mary Jane, ready to leave in a huff.

"Wait, Mary Jane. Let me have a talk with Benjie. I'll see if I can talk him into letting you join."

Jack and Benjie went into a huddle by a maple tree, just out of Mary Jane's hearing.

"What's this all about, Jack?"

"Shhh! Listen. We can't finish the go-cart because we don't have any wheels, right?"

"Right, but what makes you think that Mary Jane could help us on that? Does she have any wheels?"

"No, but that baby carriage does."

Benjie's eyes, which gleamed at the thought of the go-cart on wheels, clouded some at the thought of getting them away from Mary Jane's family buggy.

"You just let me handle it," whispered Jack, starting back to Mary Jane for the second act.

"I had a hard time, but I finally convinced Benjie to let you join – providing you contribute *your share*. But this is absolutely your only chance. And you've got to decide now, and promise not to tell anybody about what we're going to show you. Do you promise?"

In a twinkling, Mary Jane and the carriage were hustled around back of Jack's house, where the boys showed her their motoramic masterpiece. Mary Jane looked at the jumble of crate wood and planks, joined by bent spikes and roofing nails. She stood gazing at it in puzzled silence.

"Well, what do you think of it?" asked Jack, folding his arms.

Mary Jane knew she wasn't about to say the right thing, but she couldn't think of anything *else* to say.

"What is it?" she said softly, not wishing to appear ignorant.

"What is it?! It's a go-cart, naturally," said Jack, mumbling something under his breath about girls not knowing anything. "It's going to be a 'champeen' racing car when it's done. Wouldn't you like to be a part of racing history? Why, I've seen it on TV. They always have this bee-yoo-tiful movie star ride around the track before the big race. And the crowd hoots and whistles at her and gives her a big bouquet of flowers. It's just great! Wouldn't you like to be her?"

"It sounds nice," said Mary Jane. "But I'd rather be the driver."

"Well… sure, Mary Jane. You can drive…some of the time. However, remember, modern racing calls for timers, officials, mechanics, and a full pit crew."

Jack could see that he was getting through to Mary Jane, and it wasn't long before she weakened. By the time Mary Jane had returned from carrying Babsy home, the boys had blocked up the carriage and removed its wheels. When the last wheel was bolted in place, they stepped back to admire their creation. To them, it was as glorious as an Indianapolis 500 racer. The go-cart was ready to zoom, and they were eager to test drive it.

## Chapter II

# The Amazing Go-cart Test Run

"I'm first," said Jack, as he grinned over the finished go-cart. It had taken a summer of building, and years of dreaming, for this moment. It wasn't as big and grand as a clubhouse. But in his eyes, the go-cart was handsome enough to make the world sick with envy. The wire wheels off baby Babsy's buggy were like whipped cream on a pudding – the crowning touch.

The hood of the car was a box nailed to a plank, and roomy enough to put your feet in. Attached to the box were two jar lids for headlights. The steering wheel was an old tricycle wheel stuck on a broomstick. The brake was a stick, fastened with a single nail, which when pushed, rubbed against the rear wheel. The seat was an old green cushion.

"Girls should be first," said Mary Jane.

In all the excitement, Jack had almost forgotten about Mary Jane. Now, once more, he had to face the hard fact that she was a partner. And because of the wheels, they were obliged to give her a turn.

"It's too dangerous, Mary Jane. I wouldn't want you to risk your neck testing this experimental, new, never-tried-before, car. Much too risky. Isn't that so, Benjie?" Benjie's eyes were too full of the go-cart, and he was too busy rubbing his hands to hear, but he agreed with Jack, anyway.

Mary Jane pursed her lips and frowned suspiciously.

"After all," said Jack, "Are you insured for test driving?"

Mary Jane was caught off guard. She couldn't understand why she couldn't "test" drive the car as well as *anyone*. Besides, she owned the wheels!

Jack thought he'd better give an inch, before he lost a mile.

"All right, Mary Jane. You can be first… *up* the hill," said Jack.

Mary Jane climbed behind the wheel. The boys got behind the go-cart and began pushing Mary Jane up the Elm Street hill. Up the hill they trudged, as the wheels got wet going through a puddle from Mr. Yeager's lawn sprinkler, leaving a snaky trail on the sidewalk. Up, up the hill they climbed, rolling over the bumpy sidewalk in front of Mrs. McReedy's house.

"For gosh sakes, steer will you!" said Jack.

"I am," said Mary Jane, who was not about to give in. Dusty, a neighborhood dog, sniffed at them as they passed by with their strange contraption.

"All right, get off now," said Jack to Mary Jane, as they pointed the car downhill. "It's much too dangerous for you. And I couldn't stand my conscience, if I let you

14

face the danger of a test run. Why, some racers top two hundred miles an hour. Some of them crash, too!"

Mary Jane had been too busy steering, while being pushed up the hill, to give Jack any argument. She climbed out, and Jack quickly jumped into place. Benjie, just as excited as Jack, made some motor noises, as he got ready to give Jack a push. The boys had spent many days getting ready for this moment. First, there was the dream, and then all the talk about their dream, and then the planning and gathering of wood and material. Then came the building – hammer-smashing fingers and all! And finally, now, the great moment had arrived.

"Okay, Benjie," said Jack.

"Varoom, vah-room!" said Benjie, as he gave Jack a push.

Jack felt the car surge forward, and a breath of wind fan his face as the car picked up speed. Like sitting on a huge roller skate, he could feel the wheels thunder and rumble under him. Down he went, faster and faster. Things went by in a blur. Down, down he went, never putting on the brake, drinking in the thrill of it, squeezing out every last minute, till finally, with the last turn of the wheels, the car crawled to a halt.

"How'd it go?" squealed Benjie, just catching up.

"Great," said Jack. "Just great! Only, we'd better tighten up the steering a little. It's too loose."

Jack stuck his head under the box that was the hood, and made some changes. Again, Mary Jane was seated and pushed to the top of the hill.

"When am I going to have a turn to ride *down* the hill, Jack?" asked Mary Jane.

"Well, we still have to test the changes that I just made. I noticed you still had some trouble steering when we pushed you up the hill."

"That's only because I hit some of the bumps in front of Mrs. McReedy's. Next time, I'll steer around them."

"No, Mary Jane, you might get hurt. To be safe, I think Benjie should test it this time. Don't you, Benjie?"

"Yeah, yeah," said Benjie, rubbing his hands. In his hurry to get into the seat, he almost knocked Mary Jane to the sidewalk.

"Varoom, vah-room," said Benjie. And then Jack gave him a push.

The car rolled forward. Although it pulled and swerved, Benjie held it to the sidewalk, his eyes all aglow. Dusty barked at the car as it streaked by with Benjie hunched behind the wheel. Like Jack, Benjie stretched out his turn, rocking back and forth to roll farther.

Now there were many wet tracks extending from each side of the puddles caused by Mr. Yeager's lawn sprinkler. Time after time, Mary Jane got the slow ride up the hill. Then the boys would fix something, and have to "test" drive the car down the hill. Despite their efforts, the car was still not very sturdy. On one trip, a corner of the seat cushion got caught in the wheel spokes. On another trip, one of the jar lid headlights fell off. On still another trip, a wheel came loose. But with each breakdown, repairs were quickly made, while Mary Jane was beginning to smell what she thought was something rotten about this "test" driving business.

"When will it be my turn to ride *down* the hill?" said Mary Jane.

"Well, I don't think you better. The steering is slack, and I have to tighten it."

"All right for *you*, Jack, but if I don't get my turn this time, I'm going home – and I'm taking my wheels with me!"

When Mary Jane wanted to, she could be very persuasive. Jack saw that she had gotten the best of him with that argument. So, she got behind the wheel, and Jack gave her a start with a push.

Having Mary Jane as a racing partner might have worked out all right, if Rodney hadn't come along. Some things are better suffered without an audience present. Especially, if that audience includes a person who tends to snicker.

Rodney Van Skotus was the most perfect boy on the street. His mother had told him that. What's more, he *believed* it, …but none of the kids did. Rodney was one of those spotlessly clean boys who never had to wear the same shirt twice. He owned nearly every kind of toy, and they were all store-bought! He could stay up as late as he wanted. He had everything – everything but friends.

"What a crate," sneered Rodney. "I'll bet you made it yourself. What do you call that thing?"

"It's a racing car," said Benjie, ready to belt Rodney one, even though he was a head shorter.

"A racing car? Hah, hah!" laughed Rodney. "You call that thing a racing car?"

Jacked turned red, both with anger and embarrassment. He could see that Mary Jane had gone down the hill with no trouble at all. Even with Dusty barking and chasing after her all the way down.

As the boys went down the hill to bring the car back, Rodney continued to make fun of it. He was the kind of boy who could spoil things just by being around.

"You're wanted at home, Mary Jane, and right away," said Rodney. "Your mother told me she was looking for you and I told her I'd be glad to find you and send you right home."

As Mary Jane went home frustrated, the boys pushed the car back up the hill, Rodney trailing along behind. When they reached the top, he began to take the wrapper off a chocolate bar. Besides acting smart, Rodney had other bad habits. One was eating candy without sharing. He knew he got more candy than the other kids, so he ate in front of them to make their tongues hang out.

Jack had known him since kindergarten. If Rodney didn't act smart-alecky, they got along fine. But sometimes he just asked for a punch in the nose. The trouble was, he always ran for his mother, and it became a sticky time for everybody. Therefore, nobody could rassle any sense into Rodney. With his mother to fight for him, he kept on being a loudmouth, and never learned the kids' rules.

"That's rich," said Rodney. "Even a 'gur-ul' can drive that racer. Hah, hah, hah."

"Rodney always found fault with other peoples' things – especially if it was something that he wanted and didn't have. Predictably, Jack was becoming more and more annoyed by his remarks.

"Well, I bet *you* can't drive it down the hill," said Jack.

This took Rodney by surprise. "Do you wanna bet?"

"Sure. But you don't have anything to bet," said Jack, turning away.

"What do you mean? I'd bet anything, …even a million bucks!"

"That's nothing. I'm talking about betting something real. Something that you could bet right now. It's too bad you don't have anything," said Jack.

"Well, I don't have much with me *now*, only a buck," said Rodney, digging in his pockets.

A dollar was quite a lot of money to Jack, but he didn't say so. "Maybe I'd make a bet with you for a buck – *and* that candy bar you got," said Jack.

17

"Agreed. Now tell me what you'll bet me?" Rodney's acceptance was so sudden that Jack wasn't prepared for it. He shuffled his shoe on the sidewalk.

"What would you want?" he asked.

"Your jalopy," sneered Rodney.

"The go-cart?"

"That's right. If you're so sure I can't drive it, bet me. In other words – back it up or clam up!"

Jack gulped. He hadn't expected such a challenge and it caught him flat-footed. "Okay, you're on," he said.

Benjie nearly fell over. He knew that Jack was not the kind to speak without thinking, but his jaw dropped open, nonetheless. He couldn't understand how Jack would be willing to bet their go-cart, their glorious summer dream of a car. Benjie tugged at Jack's sleeve, but it didn't do any good. Rodney, having never made anything as good as this go-cart, leaped at the chance to win it.

"It's a bet, then. Stand aside. I'll show you," said Rodney.

"Just a second! When a bet's made, you have to shake on it and…"

"And what?" said Rodney.

"…and someone has to hold the bets."

"Oh, I don't know about that," said Rodney.

"Well, you'll have the racer when you go down the hill, won't you? So, a third person should hold your half of the bet. Benjie can be the third person," said Jack.

Rodney frowned a little at this, but handed over the dollar and the chocolate bar to Benjie before getting into the seat of the car.

It was a sad moment for Jack and Benjie to be giving up their car for what they figured could be its last send off. It was almost like saying goodbye to a best friend forever. Backed into a corner, Jack had taken a stupid gamble and he knew it. What he and Benjie hadn't anticipated, though, was that they were about to see the most unusual, amazing, spectacular go-cart ride in history!

From the start, the car did not steer as easily as Rodney thought it would. The front wheels waggled and flapped back and forth like a flag in the wind. Rodney was in a sweat trying to keep control of the car as it picked up speed. Faster and faster it went. Dusty, in hot pursuit, soon lagged behind and gave up the chase.

Jack and Benjie stood watching Rodney careen down the hill and weren't ready for what happened next. Neither was Rodney. It was an event which they would never forget, and one that would be retold many times, as memories were dragged out or rehashed. Before their popping eyes, the boys saw Rodney hit the worst bump in Mrs. McReedy's sidewalk. From that moment on, the go-cart was out of Rodney's hands and in the grip of fate. The car veered off the sidewalk and crashed right through Mr. Yeager's hedge, skidding onto his beautiful lawn.

Benjie was so excited, he nearly squashed the candy bar.

"Benjie, you don't think that it will…"

Before Jack could get the words out, it happened. The go-cart ran smack up to Mr. Yeager's water sprinkler and came to a stop right on top of it. For a brief glorious instant, the boys beheld a thoroughly soaked Rodney, like a statue in a fountain, with water appearing to squirt out of his ears and everywhere.

The glory did not last, however. Just as Jack and Benjie started down the hill to regain the go-cart, who should arrive on the scene but Mr. Tompkins, Mary Jane's father. He had come to reclaim the Tompkins' buggy wheels. While a drippy Rodney went bawling home to his mother, Jack and Benjie watched in silence as Mr. Tompkins removed the wheels from the cart and carried them off.

Jack had won the bet, yet lost the prize – the go-cart.

## CHAPTER III

# Yah, Yah! You Got a Girl Friend

Because of Rodney's dousing in Mr. Yeager's sprinkler, his mother raged through the neighborhood accusing and upbraiding. Jack and Benjie received most of the blame, not Rodney's steering of the go-cart or the crack in the sidewalk. After that, Rodney was, in a manner of speaking, showered with attention from his mother. She clucked over him and gave him gifts and goodies without end. Rodney had learned very early that every whimper got him some candy, and every groan, a toy. Unfortunately for Rodney, he overdid his "sick" act and ended up with a big spoonful of cod liver oil. Rodney's amazing go-cart ride marked the end of summer. With the loss of the go-cart, the rest of Jack's unfulfilled summer dreams faded as well.

"Jack! Get up, Jack!" It was morning and Jack's mother had come to get him out of bed. He was surprised to hear his mother's voice because in his dream, he was battling with a space monster. Now he woke to face a still greater threat – the first day of school! On the first day of school, Jack always jumped right out of bed. Worry over the first day always made him come wide awake. Later, as the dull routine set in, he would steal extra minutes of sleep and fight getting up. His new school clothes, with their cardboard creases, were hung near his bed. He quickly dressed, went downstairs, and sat at the table with his sister, Nancy. Jack's younger brother, Peedie, short for Philip David Holiday, was still upstairs lost in a pullover sweater, trying to find a sleeve to put his arm through.

It was always a comedy to see Peedie dress on school days. His shoelaces ended in knots that would have baffled the great Houdini. When trying to put on his trousers, he was apt to end up losing his pant leg and have one foot stuck in his pocket. He could put on his shirt inside out and backwards and still somehow get it buttoned. Peedie poked and grumbled, but his mother saw to it that he got to school just the same.

"Crunk, crinkle, crunch!" Jack was noisily eating his cereal.

Nancy frowned at Jack over the breakfast table.

"Clink, clunkle, gunch!" Jack could be an awful tease. When he was getting under somebody's skin, he'd go for the whole hide, especially that of his thin-skinned sister.

"Jack, stop crunching like that! You sound like a pig!" said Nancy.

"Crunch, crunch, gunk!"

"Ja—aa-ck! I'll tell Mom!"

'I can't help it. This kind won't wilt when it's soaked in milk."

You can *too* help it. You're doing that on purpose. So stop it! I can't stand that noise." Nancy played mother, when Mother wasn't around.

"I'll try," said Jack.

"Krink, kink, KRUNKLE!"

"Mom! MA-AH-MM!

"What is it?" called Mother.

"Jack's eating like a pig," tattled Nancy.

"Don't fool around, Jack, or you'll be late," said Mrs. Holiday, coming into the kitchen. "Oh, that Peedie. I'll be so glad when he can dress himself. This morning his clothes were so twisted, I thought his head was on wrong. Don't forget to take the pencils and notebooks I've set out for you."

"Gunkle-crunch!"

"Jack! That's enough," scolded Mrs. Holiday.

Jack made a face at Nancy because she had gotten him bawled out.

Going to school was like leaving one world and entering another for Jack. He had thoroughly explored his neighborhood and it was comfortable. He knew which dogs bit and which dogs only barked. He knew all the fences and where to climb them. He knew every tree, too, and had carved his initials in some of them. He knew the friendly from the unfriendly yards and could race through them on the blackest night. He knew where pirates might have buried gold, or Indians their dead. He knew which woods made the best jungles, where to find the best spears, and where tigers would hide if there were any. He learned a lot by himself, and the rest he learned from others, like the neat kid down the block who could touch his nose with his tongue and make his thumb double-jointed.

But school was different. In school, Jack worried about whether 'i' came before 'e' after 'c' and how many apples you could buy for ninety-eight cents and who-fought-who in the French and Indian war. As he stood at the classroom door, Jack looked like a boy out of a mail order catalog, but he felt more like a Christian about to be fed to the lions. He entered slowly to surrender himself to Ms. Rivera, his teacher for the coming year. In the room, he felt as conspicuous as a wart. His hair was slicked and barbered. His crisp new shirt collar cut his neck. And his stiff new shoes crabbed his feet.

Some of the girls stood around with silly starched smiles, but most of the boys wandered aimlessly about – looking at the bulletin boards, or staring out the windows. It was hard to work up old friendships among school chums who were so scrubbed and pressed. Mary Jane came up to Jack as if she were quite willing to forgive him for the go-cart trouble.

"Hello, Jack," said Mary Jane. Before she could ease him into conversation, however, she noticed that his attention was suddenly drawn away. Following the direction of his gaze, she saw what had caught his attention as well as that of many others in the room. There was a new girl with wavy golden hair being introduced to the teacher by her mother. The slight buzz of talk that had been going on up to this time, stopped altogether. Everyone's attention was riveted on this newcomer.

Ms. Rivera shook hands with the mother and smiled sweetly at the new girl. After a short while, the mother left and Ms. Rivera walked the new girl to the front of the room and then said, "All right, children, be seated."

Ms. Rivera watched as the scurrying children tried to get seats near their friends without knocking over the desks. The children who got the seats they wanted smiled unmercifully, while the few losers muttered to themselves. Arthur was one of the losers and was trying to push Fred off his chair.

"What seems to be the matter, boys?"

"I had my notebook here to save my place and Fred stealed my seat," said Arthur.

"You mean he stole it," corrected Ms. Rivera. Arthur had his own way of talking. It was only teachers who couldn't understand him. Kids understood him perfectly fine.

"Just sit over there for now, Joseph. I'll assign the seats later," said Ms. Rivera. Arthur continued to hang over Fred's chair.

"Why are you standing there, Joseph? I told you to be seated over *there*."

"Oh, I thought you meant him. I are Arthur, not Joseph."

'I'm sorry," said Ms. Rivera. "I will get to know your names better after we've put name tags on your desks. For now, just be seated over there, please, uh – Arthur."

Sore about losing, Arthur wanted to step on Fred's foot, but Fred had his feet safely tucked under his chair. Arthur moved to another seat. After that, the eyes of the class were once more funneled toward the new girl standing at the front of the room. All except Mary Jane, who was staring bullets at Jack.

"Now that all of you children are finally settled, I'd like to introduce to you a newcomer to our school. This is Jennifer. And I know you'll do your best to make her feel welcome. Say hello to Jennifer, children."

"Hello, Jennifer," droned the class.

From that time on, till the end of the school day, Jack hardly noticed the time slip by. His mind was so busy, he forgot he was wearing hard, wooden, new clothes that kept him from slouching.

Books were passed out and lessons begun. Jack could do well, when he set his mind to it. Every year, he started out the first day resolved to work hard and get a good report card. But he never figured out that it was necessary to start *each* day that way. So, he always wondered what happened to his high hopes in June when grades came out. When it came to school, Jack was his own worst enemy.

At dismissal time, Jack was always happy to fly from the world of education back to his comfortable neighborhood. This afternoon, he stayed after the bell.

"Uh, my name's Jack Holiday," said Jack, stumbling over his tongue.

"Nice to know you, Jack. My name's Jennifer, Jennifer Lynn."

"Yes, I know." Jack cleared his throat. "I heard. Can I carry your books for you?"

Mary Jane, watching this takes place, reached into her desk and brought out some of her books and fumbled with them.

"It's nice of you to ask, Jack, but I don't need to take my books home tonight, thank you. I finished all my assignments in our study period."

"Oh," said Jack noticeably disappointed. Mary Jane, pretending not to look, rattled her books some more and clapped another one on the top of her desk.

Jack was beginning to feel warm. He felt himself choking and stewing in his new clothes. He wanted to drop through the floor or anything, just to get away from there. Then, Jennifer came to his rescue.

"I live on Dove Street. Do you walk that way?'

"Um, sometimes," said Jack, crossing his fingers.

"What street do you live on?" asked Jennifer.

"Elm."

"Oh, that's the other way, isn't it?"

"Well, sort of. But I have to go your way today, anyhow."

Mary Jane, who overheard all of this, thumped out of the room. It seemed wonderful to Jack to leave the school walking side by side with Jennifer. It was even worth all the sideways looks and the snickers that he felt he was getting from the other boys. He'd even gotten so he could stand the hardness of his armor-plated new clothes.

"Where'd you move here from?" asked Jack

"We moved here from Pittsburgh. Have you always lived in this town?"

"Yep, this has always been my hometown."

"That's nice." said Jennifer.

"Well, yes and no," said Jack. "I rather hanker to travel. You know, like out west, to cowboy it awhile. Or sail out in the ocean and be a captain. Why, heck, I wouldn't even mind being the first explorer on Mars."

"Really?"

"Sure, why I'd much rather go to any of those places than have to go to school. And what's more, I wouldn't be afraid at all, not even going big game hunting for lions and tigers."

"Hold up, you two," came a call from behind them.

Jack turned and saw Fred running to catch up with them. If a look could make a person drop in his tracks, Jack wished he had the power to do it then to Fred.

"How come you're walking home this way, Jack? Did you move or something?" said Fred.

Jack's new clothes were getting hot on him again. Walking Jennifer home was a pleasure that Jack wanted to keep to himself. He didn't appreciate having more company. To him, Fred was being a spy and a busybody. Every time Fred said something that made Jennifer laugh, it made Jack frown. Soon they were at Jennifer's house.

"So long, Jennifer," said Fred, not knowing what a thorn he'd been in Jack's side.

"See you tomorrow, Jennifer." said Jack.

Before she went up the walk to her house, Jennifer turned, looked at Jack and said:

"You can call me Jennie."

For some time after that, Jack didn't remember where he was. He didn't remember what happened to Fred – or care. All that he thought about were Jennifer's last words, which drifted and echoed through his mind like a beautiful song. "You can call me Jennie." But he was in for a hash awakening. A block from his home, some of the neighborhood kids were waiting for him.

"Yah, yah, Jack's got a girlfriend. Jacks got a girlfriend," they taunted him.

"Dare you to come over *here* and say that, Billy Suggs," said Jack.

"What if I do?"

"I'll knock your block off, that's what," said Jack.

"You and who else?" said Billy

"C'mon, say it! Dare you to say that again!"

"Okay," said Billy thrusting out his jaw. "Jack's got a girlfriend."

"Now you've done it," said Jack. Now you've gone and done it!"

The scuffle that followed was a regular flywheel of flailing arms and legs. Jack pushed Billy. Billy pushed back. They tugged and pulled. They rolled and tumbled on the ground.

"Who says I've got a girlfriend?" said Jack, perched righteously on Billy's stomach. "Own up. Who says it?"

Billy squirmed and twisted, but saw it was no use. Jack had him pinned down.

"Tell me or I'll never let you up. Who said it?"

"It was Mary Jane who told, that's who. She told all us boys you had a girlfriend."

"Mary Jane?!" Jack was speechless. The thought of it thrashed and tossed around in his mind all the way home. Mary Jane had done this to him? But why?

When Jack got home, his mother nearly fainted at the sight of his school clothes.

"Jack, what happened to your clothes?" said Mrs. Holiday. "Have you been fighting again?"

Jack looked down at himself. His brand-new trousers were green with grass stains. His shirt had rubbed up enough dirt to grow a garden. Altogether, it was enough to make a washing machine break down and die.

Jack was scolded and put to bed early. But Mary Jane had taught him a valuable lesson. When someone is disappointed or hurt, watch out for backlash.

His gang had accused him of having a girlfriend. And he'd had to fight the truth to prove it wasn't so.

## CHAPTER IV

# Clothes, Confinement, and Columbus

It was Saturday in October. The trees had lost their summer greenness. The sky was thick with gray-black clouds that left only patches of light blue sky. The wind sounded chilly and made Jack think of warm places and warm clothes. Autumn, the season of pranks, always played tricks on Jack. Dressed too warmly, the fall weather would cook him. Dressed too lightly, an icy wind would send shivers up his back. But once he was playing, he never thought about what he was wearing. Whether warm or cold, new clothes or old, his mother always had to remind him what to put on. Forgetting caused Jack trouble.

"Jack, if I told you once, I've told you a hundred times – you're to change your clothes when you get home, and not play in your good school clothes," Mrs. Holiday said time and again.

Jack had listened, but often forgot. Peedie and Nancy had gone to play with their friends, while Jack was still at home. He was carrying out a basket of laundry for his mother to hang out to dry. In the basket were more of Jack's school clothes that he'd gotten dirty. Just like the time he had wrestled with Billy Suggs. He'd done it again. He'd muddied his good school clothes. For that reason, Mrs. Holiday was punishing him by making him stay in his own yard all day Saturday.

"Anything I can get for you at the store, Mom?" asked Jack.
Mrs. Holiday had just finished scrubbing and wringing out Jacks mud-caked laundry.

"I don't need anything at the store, thank you, Jack." said Mrs. Holiday, hanging pants, shirts, and socks on the line.

"Jack was trying his best to get back on the good side of his mother. He knew that running errands was one way of doing it, and also a way of getting away from the house. Since soiling his school clothes Thursday, Jack had been kept under house arrest. That meant that he had to come right home from school and stay in his own yard. He wasn't allowed to walk Jennifer home, or prowl through his comfortable neighborhood like a free man. With Saturday here, Jack's imprisonment became even more oppressive. All his friends were free to roam while he was stuck in solitary confinement, unless he could succeed at getting someone to come play in his yard with him.

"Are you *sure* you don't need anything at the store?" said Jack.

"Now Jack, I know what you're getting at. But it won't do any good. You have to stay in your own yard today – and that's final," said Mrs. Holiday, pinching a clothespin on the corner of a sheet.

26

Jack went to the edge of his yard and looked out. If only someone would come along, he thought. Just then, he spotted Benjie coming down the street.

"Hey, Benjie," called Jack.

Ordinarily, Jack would have run to greet Benjie or sneak up behind to scare him or something. This time, he was held back by the invisible wall that made up the boundaries to the Holiday property.

"Hi, Jack. What are you doing?" said Benjie, throwing a ball in the air and catching it.

"Just thinking," said Jack. "How about coming over to my place and having a card game? We haven't played rummy in a long time. Don't you think that'd be fun?"

Benjie made a fish-face with his lips. It was pretty plain that he didn't care for the idea.

"Well, if you don't want to play cards, how about watching cartoons with me? Bugs Bunny is on."

"Naw, I don't feel much like playing inside. I guess you're stuck at your place today, huh?" said Benjie.

"Yeah, darn it." Jack sighed.

"Gee, sorry I can't stay. Billy asked me to *his* place. We're getting up a game over in the field. We could sure use a pitcher. Couldn't you ask your mom again?"

"Wouldn't do any good. I've tried. She's made up her mind. She'll only think up a job for me to do if I keep bothering her."

"Gee, that's tough, Jack. Well, so long. Come over later, if you can.

Jack had just slumped down on his front steps feeling sorry for himself when Arthur rode up on his bicycle. Arthur pedaled right up to Jack and announced himself with a skidding, screeching stop.

"Artie!" said Jack, very much surprised and pleased to see his school chum. "How come you're over here on my street?"

Arthur was trying to balance his bicycle without touching his feet to the ground.

"I got me a job. Fred didn't want his paper route no more, so he give it to me," said Arthur.

"You mean *gave* it to you," corrected Jack.

"Yeah, that's right, for nothing. You wanna come along with me? I'll let you help me deliver papers. It's neat tossing 'em, trying to hit the porches."

"Wish I could," said Jack. "But my mom's still mad at me for wrecking my school clothes, and I gotta stay here."

"Oh. Well, I'll see ya," said Arthur, speeding off on his bike.

Jack broke up a twig into little pieces. Every place else in the neighborhood looked a million times better to him than his own yard. He threw the pieces of twig in

27

the air and then got up and paced around like a caged animal. For a little while, he stood at the hedge and watched Mr. Yeager pluck out dandelion roots. He soon tired of that and returned to the front yard. He was just in time to see Mary Jane coming down the other side of the street wheeling baby Babsy in the buggy.

Mary Jane was not Jack's first choice as a playmate. However, compared to being stuck in his prison yard alone, she was very appealing at the moment.

"Hi, Mary Jane," called Jack in his very friendliest tone of voice.

Mary Jane looked out of the corner of her eye, but didn't turn her head. She just continued to walk the buggy.

"Hey, Mary Jane. Come on over." Again, Jack called across the street but got no answer.

Mary Jane wasn't sure whether she'd scream or just plain run if Jack should come toward her. She'd caused him a lot of trouble by telling the neighborhood gang about his having a girlfriend, and she hadn't forgiven him either for walking Jennifer home. Besides, pushing the buggy reminded her painfully of the go-cart, and the spanking she got out of that. She didn't want anything to do with Jack.

Jack didn't know what was going on in Mary Jane's head. So, when she passed by, he began to think that he hadn't a friend left in all the world. Then Dusty came along.

"Here, boy. Come here, boy," Jack called to Dusty.

Dusty waddled up with a look almost like a smile. His big tail was flapping so hard that the whole dog wagged. Dusty always came happily whenever he heard his name called, whether commanded to come or not, like the times he'd go onto Mr. Yeager's lawn. Mr. Yeager would call out "Bad dog, Dusty. Go home, Dusty!" But rather than leave when ordered, Dusty would answer the call by coming instead. Then Mr. Yeager would chase him with a stone.

At least Dusty would give him someone to play with, thought Jack.

"Here, Dusty. Here, boy," called Jack, waving a stick over Dusty's head. Dusty was not a puppy anymore, and had outgrown much of his playfulness, but he seemed willing, so Jack tossed the stick.

"Go fetch it, boy. Go fetch," said Jack.

Dusty looked at Jack. He wagged his tail. He looked to where Jack was pointing and wagged his tail some more.

"Here, boy. Look." Jack picked up another stick. This time he gave Dusty a sniff of it before he threw it.

"Go get it, boy. Go on." Jack watched as Dusty lumbered out after the stick.

"That's it, boy. Get it boy."

Running, nose down, sniffing the ground, Dusty zig-zagged around the yard. The dog passed right by the stick, nearly bumping into it, but still he didn't see it. It looked like Dusty would search forever and never find it. And he probably would have, but Jack called him back.

Jack threw every stick he had. And Dusty, though appearing to try, had not fetched one. Finally, there wasn't a stick left in the yard to throw.

"Well, Dusty, ol' boy, we'll have to try something else. This time let's play 'King of the Royal Mounted.' You'll be my trusted dog companion and…"

Before Jack could finish, Dusty had spotted a cat intruding on his home ground, and like a shot, tore out after it. A good dog and cat chase can usually raise a boy's sagging spirits. But Jack, anchored to his yard, couldn't join in the chase. So again, he was left forlorn and friendless.

Jack retired to the backyard and perched himself on the family picnic table. "Boy," he thought. "If I had a clubhouse, I bet friends would come and play." Some heartaches may be worse, but the punishment of a boy stuck in his yard on a Saturday is hard to beat.

Lapsed into suffering, Jack thought of running away and becoming a hobo for life. That's what he could do. It would be the open road for him, no matter how much he'd be missed. He'd have a stick over his shoulder with a red handkerchief-bag slung on it. He'd eat his food out of tin cans, and cook over campfires. His clothes would be all patches. People would feel sorry for him. They would talk behind his back and call him a poor thing that didn't have a place to hang his hat. But that wouldn't matter to Jack. He'd wear his hat, night and day, awake or asleep, and never hang it up anyhow.

Jack had almost worn holes in his shoes with his hobo dreams, when it dawned on him that living outdoors for the rest of his life would mean giving up his favorite TV shows like 'Superman'. Before he could grapple with that problem, his hobo dreams had suddenly been snuffed out when he noticed a head peek out from hiding. It was Rodney.

Rodney ducked, but not quick enough. Jack spotted him. To Jack, Rodney represented a last hope. Otherwise, he would be doomed to his lonely island like Robinson Crusoe. He must, somehow, get Rodney to stay in the yard and play with him. Jack's brain whirred into action.

"Heave ho on the mainmasts," Jack called, as he grabbed one of the clothes poles and propped it against the picnic table with the sheet still hanging on the line overhead. "Get to the shrouds, unfurl the sails, ye lubbers." Jack saw Rodney creep closer and hide behind one of the sheets hanging on the line. Jack still pretended not to see Rodney, as he went on building the set for his little play. He put the clothes basket on the picnic table.

"Ahoy, lookout in the crow's nest! Have ye sighted land yet?" called Jack.

"Finally, Rodney couldn't stand it any longer. He had to give in to his curiosity.
"What are you doing, Jack?" asked Rodney, scratching his head.

"What am I doing?! Do you know what day is coming up? Well, do you?"

Rodney shook his head and scratched some more.

"Well, it's Columbus Day, that's what. And this is the good ship, *Santa Maria*,"
said Jack, tapping his toe on the picnic table. "After we discover the new world, this
ship'll hit a rock and sink. And we'll send out distress signals to the *Nina* and *Pinta*
to come to our rescue. You can be one of the crew."

"What do I have to do?" asked Rodney.

"What do you have to do?! Don't you know anything about history? Why, when
we land on the shore of the New World, you'll be one of the Spanish soldiers and
build a fort to make friends with the natives."

"What would I do that for?"

"Because you want to discover which islands have gold, naturally. Later, you
burn down their villages and put the natives in chains to get them to confess where
the gold is hid. It'll be a smacking good time, Rodney. Do you wanna play?"

"Okay. But who will *you* be?"

"Oh, I'll be Christopher Columbus. And I'll have to sail back to Europe
sometimes to beg Queen Isabella for more time and money to pay for the ships. First,
let's take those sticks behind the garage and make some swords."

# Holidays and Hoopla

With all the excitement around Jack's picnic table, the *Santa Maria* soon attracted a full crew. Joining Rodney as sailors were Billy and Benjie, and later Artie, who had finished delivering his newspapers. Jacks brother, Peedie, was turned into a friendly native. And Dusty, it was decided, would be one of the wild beasts of the islands. Nancy put on a robe and some fake jewels, and played Queen Isabella.

Jacks mother heard all the noise and looked out her kitchen window. When she saw all the fun Jack was having sword fighting, she heaved a big sigh and threw her arms in the air. Mrs. Holiday wondered how she could ever succeed in teaching Jack a lesson about ruining his school clothes, when he was having that much fun. And anyway, she didn't have the heart to bawl out such a big hero as Christopher Columbus.

## CHAPTER V

# Aunts, Uncles, and Ghosts

"Jack! Nancy! Peedie! Come home, kids!" called Mrs. Holiday.

"What do you want, Mom?" said Jack, running up a second later, with Peedie trailing behind.

"Your Aunt Lulu is here and she'd like to see all of you."

"Aw, Mom, do we have to? We were just making plans to build something."

"Now, Jack, Aunt Lulu doesn't come to visit us very often. And she'll only be here for the weekend. The least you can do is spend some time with her. You and Peedie go tell Nancy that she has to come home right away. I think she must be playing with Mary Jane."

Jack and Peedie walked at a snail's pace over to Mary Jane's house. As they walked, Jack grumbled to himself that it meant lousing up his weekend. Like last Saturday, when he was punished for ruining his school clothes, he would be stuck at home again – only this time it was to visit with Aunt Lulu. Nancy was playing with dolls with Mary Jane when the boys found her.

"Nancy, you have to come home."

"Who says?"

"Mom does. Aunt Lulu is here. And Mom says we've got to stick around home and visit with her." Giving Nancy this message held some small satisfaction for Jack. At least he knew he wouldn't have to suffer his aunt's visit all by himself. Nonetheless, Nancy continued to dress her doll.

"I'll be along when I'm good and ready," said Nancy, who hated to be told anything by Jack.

"Okay, but don't forget I told you so. Peedie and I'll start back, and you can catch up."

The falling leaves were gathering on the sidewalk like big corn flakes, and the boys shuffled paths through them. For once, Peedie was able to keep up with Jack as he dragged along.

"Who is Aunt Lulu, Jack?" asked Peedie.

"She's your aunt. You probably don't remember her because you were pretty little when she visited us last."

"What's she look like?"

"She's big. That's about all I remember. Oh, and she wears these big brooches."

"Brooches?"

"Yeah, you know, a brooch is a big pin a lady wears on the front of her dress. It's shaped like a flower or something and has sharp pointed leaves around broken pieces of colored glass. Watch out when she goes to hug you that she doesn't grab you on the side with the brooch. She hugs so tight, she nearly mangles your bones. And if you get squeezed on the side with the brooch, you darned near get stabbed to death."

"Gosh, I'll watch out for it. Does she have any kids of her own?" said Peedie.

"Naw. She's big enough to, but she doesn't. Wish she did. Then she could bring them along and we'd have someone to play with. And she wouldn't have to hug *us* to pieces. Hey, let's stop here and wait for Nancy. We don't want to get home *too* soon.

"Jack?" said Peedie, with a worried look on his face.

"Yeah?"

"About that,… that brooch."

"What about it?"

"Which side does she wear it on?"

"Oh, you worried about that? I don't remember which side. But it sticks out, so you'll be able to spot it quick enough. Just don't let her point it at you when she goes to hug you. Move to the other side."

Soon, Nancy came along and the boys didn't have any more excuse to dilly dally. They walked on the sidewalk all the way, instead of taking their regular shortcuts across lots or over lawns. The screen door banged behind them as Jack entered and said:

"Mom, I think Peedie and I should get washed up before we see Aunt Lulu, don't you?"

"Why, yes, Jack. I think that would be a good idea. Be sure Peedie scrubs behind his ears."

Jack and Peedie went upstairs to wash up. For a long time, they dawdled and played with the soap, squeezed water through the wash rag, and splashed and made suds. It wasn't much fun, but it did waste time. Nancy had gone right in the living room to see Aunt Lulu. She was braver about facing relatives than Jack.

"How come Nancy went right away to see Aunt Lulu, Jack?" asked Peedie.

"You know how she loves attention."

"Oh," said Peedie, pricking a big bubble with his finger.

"Boys!" called Mrs. Holiday from downstairs.

"We'd better get down there pretty quick, or Mom'll be mad at us. Let me see behind your ears. Yuk! Hold still while I get some of that dirt off."

"Not so hard, Jack!" Peedie always winced when he was scrubbed with soap and water. And, besides, he had another thought.

"Do me a favor, Jack. Don't get all the dirt off."

"Why not?"

"Maybe Aunt Lulu won't want to hug me too tight if I got dirt on me."

"It won't help any. I think she's near-sighted. Hurry up and dry yourself off before Mom gets mad at us.

With every last dodge used up, the boys approached the steps leading downstairs. Peedie and Jack looked at each other. They might have burst out laughing, if it hadn't seemed so grim to them. They could hear Aunt Lulu talking sweetly to Mother and Nancy. Somehow, it always makes Jack feel sour inside to hear his aunt talk so sugary. Peedie, with a pleading look in his eyes, wanted Jack to go first, and so he did. They came down one step at a time feeling like the eyes of the world were upon them.

"Jack and Peedie," gushed Aunt Lulu, nearly swooning. "Dear, dear boys. Let me have a look at you. My, how you've grown – and Nancy, too. I simply can't get over it. Why, it seems like just yesterday when you were such wee little helpless things. Now here you are, grown into regular little ladies and gentlemen. Come here and give your Auntie a big hug."

'Uh, oh. Here it comes,' thought Peedie, hanging behind Jack. He had already spotted the brooch that Jack had warned him about. It was a big metallic star with spikes jutting out every which way.

Jack went up and took his hug like a soldier. Peedie still hung back, whistling silently to himself.

"Peedie, can you give your Aunt Lulu a hug?" said Mrs. Holiday, hoping that no unfortunate accidents would happen.

Peedie stepped forward and, with a gritty smile, took his hug. He very carefully steered to one side – the side without the brooch. During the hug, which seemed to Peedie to last a lifetime, he stopped breathing. He found he *had* to, partly from being squeezed, but mostly because he couldn't stand Aunt Lulu's perfume. Finally, when Aunt Lulu released Peedie, he said:

"What's that smell?!"

"Peedie," said Mother, to ward off a social blunder. You'd better go let the cat out." Peedie left the room.

"Where's Uncle Ollie?" asked Jack. Didn't he come along with you?" Jack had almost forgotten Uncle Oliver. Somehow, in his mind, Aunt Lulu always loomed so much larger than her husband.

"Uncle Oliver is. . . uptown," said Mrs. Holiday. "He'll be here later."

"Oh," said Jack, disappointedly. Uncle Oliver always had tricks and fun stories to tell.

Later, Aunt Lulu dragged out some beautifully gift-wrapped packages for Peedie, Nancy, and Jack. For bringing the presents, Aunt Lulu got another hug apiece from each of the children. Peedie was so excited about getting a present that he forgot and got on the side where his aunt wore the prickly brooch. Like being squished in an iron maiden, he was jabbed with the spiky points of the pin. Peedie would suffer most anything to get a present, though, and could hardly wait to tear the wrappings off his. Jack and Nancy opened their gifts more slowly. Both had gotten presents from Aunt Lulu before.

Jack got a blue prayer book, and Nancy got a purple prayer book with a red book-marker. Peedie's present was a picture to hang on the wall. The picture showed a very tidy bedroom with a boy and a girl with big eyes and haloes over their heads, kneeling by a bed saying their prayers. A motto underneath read: "Except ye become as little children, ye shall not enter Heaven." Another round of hugs followed. This time, however, Peedie carefully avoided the thorny star.

At six o'clock, Mr. Holiday joined Aunt Lulu and his family at the supper table. The children were cautioned to watch their manners. Everything went smoothly, other than when Peedie dropped some mashed potatoes in his lap.

It wasn't until evening that Uncle Oliver returned from town. Uncle Oliver was a marvelously round and jolly fellow. The most noticeable thing about him was his shiny nose, which was almost the size of a round, red, Christmas ball. Jack and Nancy ran up to meet him as he entered. Peedie hung back, but was still very curious.

"Tell us a story, Uncle Ollie," said Nancy, jumping up and down.

"Children, I think it's time to get to bed," said Mrs. Holiday.

"You hadn't better tell them a story tonight, Oliver. The little dears need their rest," said Aunt Lulu.

"Oh please, Uncle Ollie. We don't have school tomorrow. Just one story."

Finally, Mr. Holiday settled the matter by saying:

"Get your pajamas on first. Then if Uncle Ollie is willing, you can have a story upstairs in your bedroom."

Jack and Nancy scooted up the stairs, and Peedie skiddled after. It wasn't long before they were dressed, in bed, and ready for a story.

Before long, Uncle Oliver made his way upstairs to the delight of the children.

"What kind of a story would you like?" said Uncle Oliver, settling down on the edge of Jack's bed.

"Tell us a spooky one," said Jack.

"Let me think," said Uncle Oliver, gathering his thoughts.

*"Once upon a time, there was a wicked prime minister with a long spidery beard."*

"What's a prime minister?" asked Peedie.

"He's the helper next to the king, for this story takes place a long time ago in another land which was ruled by a king and his prime minister. The prime minister's name was Peter Peppercorn, and he lived with the king in a big old stone castle. The castle had a moat around it.

"What's a moat?"

"Don't interrupt, Peedie," said Jack.

"A moat," answered Uncle Oliver, "is a deep, wide ditch filled with water. To get into a castle, it was often necessary to cross a moat over a drawbridge."

"What's a drawbridge?"

"Stop interrupting, stupid," said Nancy, "Or we won't be able to hear the whole story."

"A drawbridge," Uncle Oliver went on, "is a bridge that's hinged and can be hauled up with chains so that nobody can get in. When the bridge was lowered, it would sound like this – *clink, clank, clank, clank, clank, clank, FUMP!*

*"One day, the king was killed mysteriously. The prime minister had always claimed to have magic to protect the king. But since he was apparently unable to prevent the king's death, and therefore, likely to lose his job, he pretended that the*

*king was still alive. He hid the king's body by dropping it into a deep well outside the walls of the castle. That way, no one would know the king was actually dead.*

*To keep the villagers from learning that the king was dead, Peppercorn had to pretend that the king was still alive. He told them that the reason they didn't see the king around anymore, was that he was up in the tower talking with spirits. The superstitious townspeople were comforted when Peppercorn told them that the king would soon be down to see them. Still, people kept asking to see the king, and so Peter Peppercorn had to make up ghost stories to scare the people from snooping around the castle. He also posted a guard at the gate and ordered him not to open the drawbridge for anybody, but himself or the king. He noted the king, for he always had to be careful to talk as if the king still lived.*

*Some of the villagers, who had known the king, believed what Peppercorn told them and expected to see the king again. But most of the people either didn't know or didn't care. After all, if the prime minister wanted people to stay away and not see inside the castle, that was his right – he was next in power and could speak for the king. And if the king remained hiding, that was his business. So the villagers didn't pay much attention to Peppercorn, the castle, or even miss the king much.*

*As time passed and more people were waiting to see the king, Peter Peppercorn had to make up more and more stories about the king talking to spirits, or else be caught in his lies and lose his job. The more ghost stories he made up, the more he scared himself. Each night, the prime minister would climb the crooked stairs leading to his tower bedroom. The stairs would creak like this – screech-squawk, screech-squawk, screech-squawk! Then he would close his big door on its rusty hinges that would shut like this – der-r-r-blam! Then he would turn the key in his lock – klinkity-klinkle!.*

*One dark misty night, a night when bats liked to flutter about, Peter Peppercorn locked himself in his tower bedroom, lit his candles to chase the scary shadows, and jumped into his bed. He'd just gotten under the covers, when he heard a loud noise. It went – clink, clank, clank, clank, clank, clank, clank, FUMP! He knew it was the drawbridge, so he sat up in bed and carefully listened. Next, he heard – screech-squawk, screech-squawk, screech-squawk. He knew someone or something was climbing the stairs. And he thought of the ghosts he had told the people about. He shivered and jumped out of bed. Next, he tried to see through his keyhole when he heard something in the lock. It went – klinkity-klinkle! He stood back from the door as far as he could. Then he saw the door move – ker-r-r-r.*

*Frightened by all the ghosts that he had imagined in his own mind, poor Peter Peppercorn was certain that behind the moving door was a ghost – maybe the ghost of the king, whom he'd hidden in the well. Could it be that the well-keeper had discovered the dead king in the well and was coming to report it? Well, before the*

*door was fully open, Peppercorn stepped backward, slipped, and fell out the tower*
*window and dropped to his death in the moat!"*

"And do you know what that goes to show?"
"No, what, Uncle Ollie?"
"If you spread lies, they'll return to haunt you."
"Gosh, that was a good ghost story," said Jack.
Before Uncle Oliver turned out the lights, he said, "Night, Jack!"
"Goodnight, Uncle Ollie."
"Night, Nancy."
"Goodnight."
"Night, Peedie. Don't have any nightmares, will you?
"N-n-n-no! I hope not," Peedie said, pulling the covers up almost over his head.

CHAPTER VI

# Antics of An Acrobatic Fly

After chicken dinner, Sunday, Aunt Lulu and Uncle Ollie ended their visit with the Holidays. The weekend was over. The only excitement had been Uncle Ollie's ghost story and a bad dream that followed it. Peedie had a nightmare, and during it, walked in his sleep and tossed Butterball, the cat, out the window. Peedie, still asleep, was put back to bed. And soon everyone else was back to sleep, too. All except the cat, who was still a bit rag-tailed. Mr. and Mrs. Holiday thought it was lucky that Peedie hadn't fallen out the window, but Butterball thought differently. He yowled all night outside Mr. Yeager's bedroom window, and for his trouble, got beaned with a shoe. It just wasn't Butterball's night.

Monday, Jack, Peedie, and Nancy found themselves back in school.

"Jennifer, will you please lead the class in saying the Pledge of Allegiance this morning?" said Ms. Rivera.

Jack watched as Jennifer went to the front of the room, faced the flag, clasped her hand over her heart, and began the pledge.

With Jennifer leading the pledge, Jack's voice boomed with more than its usual patriotism. His enthusiasm was noticed by Mary Jane, who stuck him with her pencil as he went to sit down and called him a showoff.

Ms. Rivera, aware of some murmuring in Jack's corner of the room, sent a cross look in that direction, and then said:

"Now children, we will turn to page twenty three in our arithmetic books. Please do the problems which I have listed on the board. Any questions?"

Arthur raised his hand.

"Yes, Arthur. What is it?"

"I done that page yesterday."

"You mean '*did*' that page," corrected Ms. Riviera.

"Yeah, that's what I mean. I got that all did."

"You must not have listened very well, Arthur, because our assignment yesterday was page twenty two."

"Maybe that's why my answers is all marked wrong."

"That may be, Arthur. You usually do get a few right. After this, please double check to be sure you are doing the right page. Bring your paper up to my desk while the rest begin today's arithmetic."

While Arthur went to the front of the room, Jack looked down at the arithmetic problems in front of him. The harder he tried to fasten on the first problem, the more the numbers were swimming before him. He stared at the paper. The paper stared

39

back. He began his attack on it again, tracing over his name at the top of the page. It seemed to him that his signature was much too plain and uncurly. He promised himself to design a fancier signature for the future, in case he should ever be called upon to sign a Declaration of Independence or something.

It was hard for Jack to sit with his knees knuckled under a desk. He thought of the picture in his social studies book of Socrates, the famous Greek philosopher, standing outdoors, teaching his students who were sitting or lying down on the grass. There was no doubt in Jack's mind why Socrates was the greatest teacher. Jack looked out the window. Away off, the swaying trees seemed alive, as if beckoning him to climb them. Sometimes he could hear the whine of the wind, or the roar of a truck, or the bark of a dog. Out there was the kind of freedom he dreamed of. He envied the truck driver, who was going different places, seeing different things. He envied the dog for just being outside.

A buzzing brought Jack's attention back to his desk. A fly had landed on his arithmetic book. It appeared to be checking his arithmetic problems. Jack's cupped hand sneaked up on the fly with all the cunning of a hunter.

*'I must seem like a big giant to him'*, thought Jack as his hand crept up. *'What's being big to a fly, anyhow? It can walk upside down on the ceiling and I can't.'* Jack's hand swept across the book. At first, Jack thought he had missed, but then he put his clenched fist to his ear and shook it. He got his answer from hearing a buzz and feeling a little tickle in his hand.

*'Toward winter, flies are always kind of lazy,'* thought Jack. He stole a glance toward the teacher to see if he'd been seen. Ms. Rivera was busy at her desk. But the moment his eyes fell upon her, she looked up and caught his glance. Jack, who always felt the look on his face gave him away, dropped his eyes and went furiously back to work on his arithmetic.

Later, when Jack felt that the heat of Ms. Rivera's attention was off him, he inspected his catch. He opened his hand very slowly. He expected that the fly might zoom away. Looking into the hollow of his hand, he could see the little creature looking back at him with its honeycombed eyes.

*'Any second now it will fly away,'* thought Jack. But it didn't. It crouched on his hand like a featherweight boxer. It held this stance for some time. Then when no danger seemed present, the fly relaxed, rubbed its forelegs together, and polished its socketed head. The fly's two little cellophane-like wings did not seem to be hurt, but still it did not fly away. Jack guessed that it must have lost its power to fly, and studied it as it paraded across his desk.

"All right, children. Put your arithmetic books and papers away, and get ready for lavatory," said Ms. Rivera. Lavatory was one of the better parts of the school day. It was a time when you could walk around and maybe, if you were quiet enough, chat a bit with a friend. Jack gathered his fly and put him in his pencil box for safekeeping.

After lavatory, Ms. Rivera announced that they were going to have a spelldown. Everyone else had been given a word when it came to Arthur's turn. Arthur always tried to hide himself in the room so he would be the last to be called on – or perhaps forgotten, altogether. A few students had been seated by misspelling their word, but most were still standing.

"And now, Arthur," said Ms. Rivera. "Spell pict-CHEWer. The pict-CHEWer is on the wall. Pict-CHEWer."

"Oh, geez," said Arthur, his face twisting with the torment of a martyred saint. "What was it you give me again?"

"Pict-CHEWer."

"Oh yeah, pitcher," said Arthur, his eyes searching back into his head. "Let's see. P,…um, that's it. Uh, P,…I,…CH—ER!"

"That's not right, Arthur. Spell Pict-CHEWer, Jennifer," said Ms. Rivera.

"Picture. P-I-C…T-U-R-E." Jennifer was one of the best spellers in the class.

"That's right, Jennifer. Arthur, why are you still standing?" asked Ms. Rivera.

"Didn't I get my word right?"

"No, you did not."

"Oh," said Arthur, taking his seat. "I musta thunk wrong."

Five minutes later, only six players remained in the spelling bee: Jennifer, Jack, Mary Jane, Susan, Betty, and Rodney.

"Jack, your word is 'Decide'. Please help us to 'decide'."

Jack stepped forward and said:

"Decide. D-E-S-I-D-E."

"I'm sorry, Jack. That is incorrect. Jennifer, you spell Jack's word," said the teacher.

For once in her life, Jennifer looked uncomfortable. Like she was about to receive a shot in the arm or worse. The room grew still. No one fidgeted.

"Come, Jennifer. We're waiting," said Ms. Rivera.

Jennifer looked at Ms. Rivera, glanced toward the floor, but she could not look at Jack. She shook her head to herself and then said in a voice barely heard:

"Decide. D-I-S-I-D-E."

"Why Jennifer, I'm surprised at you. Children, it looks like we may end up with a new spelling champion today – provided *someone* is able to spell the word 'decide'."

Jennifer went to her seat. And Jack beamed a look of comfort and adoration in her direction. Rodney was next. He looked ready to leap out of his shoes with eagerness. At that moment, Jack wished he had the gorgon's power to turn men to stone with a glance. But lacking this desirable power, all he could do was blaze away at Rodney with his eyes.

"Rodney, can *you* spell 'decide'?" asked Ms. Rivera.

Rodney stepped forward with a smirk as broad as a canyon.

"Yes, I can spell it," said Rodney. "D-E-C-I-D-E!"

The spelldown continued until all the children were seated, except Mary Jane and Rodney, who were then called the winners. Rodney was so proud of out-spelling Jennifer that he was impossible to sit near. He sat up like a stick and looked as comfortable as a skunk. The more he bragged about winning, the more glum Jennifer became. The more glum she became, the more Jack rankled and thirsted to get Rodney.

"Now children, get out your science books and be sure to go over the questions at the end of the chapter." Ms. Rivera looked around the room to be sure everyone was reading. Then she spotted Arthur and said:

"No, Arthur. I said to read your science book, not your social studies."

"Oh yeah, my mistake. The covers are the same color of purple."

# Holidays and Hoopla

The morning crawled to afternoon. And all day long, Rodney was insufferable. Every chance he got, he made fun of Jennifer. He boasted of beating her in spelling to any ear he could latch onto. It was more than Jack could stomach. Jack's brow crouched with rage, his eyes narrowed with fury, and his soul demanded satisfaction. But, lacking an opportunity to clobber Rodney in the classroom, Jack had to satisfy himself with the thought of getting him during recess. In the meantime, he took up his book and stuck his nose into it. His interest began to sag reading the dreary printed facts. And then he remembered the fly in the pencil box. Was the fly still alive? Or had it passed on to fly heaven? Jack opened the box. The fly was waiting, balanced on a pencil like a lumber jack on a log. Jack brought the pencil out and set the fly on his desk. Hidden behind his propped-up book, Jack watched the fly parade across his desk and climb his math book. The fly became a regular one-fly circus. The talented fly soon caught the eye of Fred and others who sat near Jack.

As Jack's performing fly collected an audience, he put it through more gyrations than a trick dog. He had the fly crawling through hoops and walking on a piece of paper upside down. Such a performance was bound to attract widespread attention, which it did – Ms. Rivera's.

"Jack, whatever you're fooling with, get rid of it this minute." Ms. Rivera was not one whose wishes could be trifled with. Her lightning commands, if disregarded, were followed by thunder. While Ms. Rivera scolded Jack, Rodney turned around in his seat and, with a simper of priggish delight, flashed his unfortunate smile at Jack. Jack could take scolding, but he could not stand the jeers of a sideline hyena. In Rodney's snickering smile, Jack saw all the mockery of the world – all the ridicule which could be, or ever was. In Rodney's face in that instant, Jack saw every mama's boy, teaser, and tattletale. And most of all, he saw what he considered the reason for Jennifer's loss in the spelling bee.

"Turn around, Rodney. It's none of your business," said Ms. Rivera.

Jack stood up from his desk and headed up the aisle holding in his hand the piece of paper with the fly clinging to it. As he drew near Rodney on his way to the waste basket, Jack could almost imagine eyes snickering out from the back of Rodney's head. How he ached to wipe off the smug look that he knew was on Rodney's face. It was then the idea hit him. In a flash, it was done. Jack knuckle-flicked the fly off the paper onto Rodney.

The fly slid down into Rodney's shirt collar so smoothly, it almost seemed planned. Rodney didn't feel it slip down his collar. Jack continued to the front of the room, dumped the scrap paper into the basket, and returned to his desk and sat down. The suspense was killing him, but Jack kept as calm as an astronaut waiting for blast-off.

Ms. Rivera had just stepped to the front of the room to pull down the map for social studies, when it happened. The event was so startling that she let loose of the map before it stuck down. It flew up like a window shade with a whirr and a clank. Mary Jane had noticed that Rodney had become unusually twitchy. She was absolutely astounded when he began leaping around like a go-go dancer. Unable to hold back, Rodney burst out in fits of laughter – for the fly had evidently worked into a ticklish place.

"Rodney! What are you doing?" said Ms. Rivera, as she watched him leap and bellow around the room.

"I-I-I can't help it, Ms. Rivera. Whoa –o-o…" said Rodney, and he was off again – as the fly apparently found another ticklish spot.

It wasn't long before the exasperated Ms. Rivera had ushered the giggling, wiggling, Rodney down to the nurse's office. There she suggested that he should have a complete medical examination. All the rest of the day, the class buzzed with surprise and amazement. All but Jack, who was forever grateful to that fly for settling a score for him.

## CHAPTER VII

# Leapin' Leaf Pile

"I think the leaves should be raked up today," said Mr. Holiday over the breakfast table. He took another sip of coffee as Mrs. Holiday buttered some toast.

"By the way, where's Jack this morning?"

"He isn't out of bed yet," said Mrs. Holiday.

"Well, when he does get up, tell him to get the leaves raked up in front."

"That's not going to make him very happy, Frank, having to stay around the yard. You remember two weeks ago I made him stay in the yard because he ruined his school clothes. And last weekend, Aunt Lulu and Uncle Ollie were here. It'll mean *another* Saturday stuck in his own yard."

"A little yard work won't hurt him. Besides, Nancy and Peedie can pitch in and help, too. I've got to go uptown to get some anti-freeze in the car radiator. We'll be getting our first frost soon."

As Mr. Holiday backed the car out of the driveway, Jack was upstairs buttoning his shirt and continuing to think about the fly he'd dropped down Rodney's collar. Rodney sure had put on a show, bellowing and leaping around the room. And nobody had found out what caused his sudden ticklishness – not even the school nurse – so Jack hadn't been blamed. As Jack thought about it now, he wasn't very proud of what he had done. He was even a little ashamed. He wasn't sure what had made him do it. It seemed funny enough at the time. But, really, Rodney wasn't such a bad kid, once you got to know him. If only he wouldn't be such a pill, and act so snooty and brag so much. But perhaps Rodney couldn't help being what he was, any more than Jack could help dumping the fly down his collar.

An hour later, Jack was out on the front lawn with Peedie and Nancy. At first, they merely looked at the scads of orange and yellow leaves scattered about the yard. The job looked nearly impossible to do. Jack stood leaning on his rake. Mancy sat in the wagon and watched Peedie ride his rake around like a horse.

Mrs. Holiday looked out the front door. She saw that they hadn't started yet, and said:

"Children, you'll never get the leaves raked up just looking at them. Dad will be home as soon as he gets the car winterized. If you don't have the job done by then, he's going to be awfully mad. He wants to get rid of those leaves today."

"It's not fair, Mom. Look at Peedie. He's no help at all." Peedie was still galloping around on the rake-like horse.

"Peedie, you stop playing horsey and help Jack. You too, Nancy." Mrs. Holiday watched as the children began to rake the leaves, then she returned to her own housework. The children worked very hard at first. Then Jack said:

"Nancy, why aren't you bringing more leaves over to the pile?"

"I'm getting as many as Peedie," she answered.

"That's the trouble. If you only get as many as Peedie, that's not very many."

"Well, I can't help it. Every time I fill up the wagon, the leaves fall out the sides."

I've got an idea, Nancy. Go get the big tarp out of the garage."

"Tarp? What's a tarp?"

"A tarp is a tarpaulin. You know, that big piece of canvas cloth. We use it for a tent sometimes."

"What good is that?"

"Don't ask silly questions, Nancy. Just get it and I'll show you."

Jack kept raking while Nancy went to the garage to get the canvas. As his rake swept the leaves along, they would take wing, soar into the air, skim, hover, and land – only to be hurled forward by the rake once more, until they were whisked into the pile. The rake, when dragged across the sidewalk, scraped and made Jack's teeth chatter. Raking leaves was work. But it was fun, too, with the rays of the sun making everything golden.

Peedie had the garden rake with the hard, short, stubby, teeth that snagged in the grass.

"Peedie, what are you stopping for?" said Jack.

"I can't work this dumb thing, Jack. You always take the best rake for yourself. Why can't I use *your* rake?"

Jack had the lawn rake with the long springy tines. He knew that his rake worked better than Peedie's, but he also knew that he could rake more leaves than Peedie could. So after showing Peedie how he might make the garden rake work better, Jack kept the lawn rake for himself. Peedie kept mumbling how his rake didn't work good. He would have continued to grumble, if Nancy hadn't come down the driveway at that minute tugging the big canvas behind her.

"Ugh!" groaned Nancy. "Here it is, Jack. Now that I've dragged it out here, what are you going to do with it?"

"Let me show you. Help me lay it out flat. Peedie, get off it! Okay, grab up as many leaves in your arms as you can and load 'em on the canvas."

When the canvas was nearly hidden under leaves, Jack pulled the four corners of the tarpaulin into a bunch and slung it over his shoulder.

"You look like Santa Clause with that bag, Jack," said Peedie, a smile sparkling across his face.

Just then, Benjie came by.

"What are you doing, Jack?" he asked.

"What's it look like?" Jack dumped the leaves onto the pile.

"You going to jump in 'em?"

'Sure, maybe. You want to help?

"Okay."

"Help me lay this canvas out flat again, then."

After Benjie had helped get the canvas stretched flat, Jack looked around in all directions.

"Now where is that Peedie? Just when there's a job to be done, he up and disappears."

"Here I am!" Peedie giggled as he poked his leafy head out through the top of the pile.

"Stop fooling around, Peedie, or we'll never get these leaves raked up."

"It's your fault, Jack. You dumped that last load of leaves on top of me."

"Oh yeah, sure. Get busy and help. You too, Nancy... Nancy! What are you doing there, fooling with that one leaf?"

"This leaf's so pretty, I'm going to press it and take it to school Monday."

"You're just wasting time. Get busy and help."

"Psst. Hey Jack, look! Billy Suggs is coming up the street. Let's hide on him," said Benjie.

"Okay, quick! Everybody into the pile."

Benjie, Nancy, and Peedie scrambled into the pile, and Jack made sure they were well hidden before he wiggled in, himself. The four hardly dared to breathe, waiting for Billy to walk by. Peedie almost gave them away. He felt a sneeze coming on, but he caught it in the nick of time. Soon, Billy was right by the pile.

Then, they all sprung out at Billy like jumping jacks and shouted:

"Boo!"

"Yikes!" said Billy, startled to see the pile of leaves explode.

"Boy, did you jump a mile!" laughed Jack.

"Aw, you didn't scare me," said Billy. "I thought the pile looked kinda funny all the time."

"Isn't it neat?" said Benjie, rubbing his hands together. "Did you ever see such a big pile of leaves in your life?"

"I've seen bigger," Billy said.

"Bigger than this?"

"Sure, much bigger."

"I bet."

"Bet you anything."

"It doesn't matter anyway," said Jack, breaking up the argument. "We're not finished making our pile, yet. You want to join us, Billy?"

"Maybe. But what do you mean you're not through making your pile. Looks to me like you've got every leaf in the yard on that pile." Billy's eyes scanned the Holiday yard.

Yeah, but there's lots more leaves on this *street*. In *your* yard for instance, and Benjie's, and Mary Jane's."

After hearing Jack's words, the kids craned their necks up and down the street, nodding their heads, impressed with all the leaves to be had on the street. Then began perhaps the most astonishing, ambitious, leaf gathering in history.

Nobody gave much thought to whether Jack's dad would appreciate more leaves on his property, but they all pitched in and rounded up leaves throughout the whole neighborhood, carrying them to Jack's yard. And as the pile grew in size, the helpers grew in number. Mary Jane and Rodney then joined the project as well.

The pile grew so large, it even dwarfed Jack and Billy. Its width and sprawl covered the lawn and blocked part of the sidewalk. The more it towered to the sky, the more it spread over the Holiday's lawn – even overflowing its boundary lines. Such a mountain of leaves had never before been seen on Elm Street. The nearest thing to Jack's leaf gathering gang were probably the pyramid builders of ancient Egypt.

When the pile was finished, the children began jumping in the leaves. The job had been peppered with fooling around, but now it was *all* play. They pranced. They vaulted. They plunged. They bounced and scrimmaged and frolicked till the mountainous pile had worn down to a foothill.

"Hold it, gang. Let's fix up the pile," said Jack. Billy took another lunge into what was left of the pile and wallowed in it.

"I said hold it, Billy, 'til we fix up the pile again!"

In a jiffy, the scattered leaves were fluffed up into a pile once more.

"This time, let's take turns jumping in the pile instead of having a free-for-all. Mary Jane can be first, then Nancy, Peedie, Benjie, Rodney, me, and then you, Billy."

"How come I'm last, Jack?" asked Billy.

"Because you jumped in the pile last. That's why."

Billy mumbled something to himself about that not making any difference, but he stood back while Mary Jane tumbled into the pile first, followed in short order by Nancy.

"Look at me," said Peedie, who then took a running nose-dive into the pile.

"That's nothing. Watch this!" Benjie somersaulted into the pile. – THWACK!

"Hey!"

"What's that?" said Benjie.

"Me, that's what." It was Peedie. He was buried in the pile as Benjie somersaulted in. This caused them to bump into each other.

"Oh, sorry about that, Peedie. I didn't see you were in there."

Rodney was just about ready to take his sprint, when Billy jostled him and lurched into the pile ahead of him."

"Hey, that's no fair, Billy. You went ahead of your turn," complained Rodney.

"You're too pokey," Billy snapped back.

"I was waiting for Benjie and Peedie to move out of the way."

"Why don't you run to your mother about it, sissy boy," said Billy, giving Rodney a push.

"Wait a minute, Billy," said Jack. "If we're going to jump one at a time in the pile, the only fair way is to take turns. You've had your turn, now it's Rodney's and mine."

"I'll take a turn whenever I darn well please. I helped make this pile."

"So what. So did all the others," said Jack. "If you won't take turns like all the rest, you can get out of my yard. This is my property.

"Yeah? Well, some of the leaves came from my place, so it belongs as much to me as you."

"Yeah?"

"Yeah!"

The fight that followed was better than anything on TV. Billy shoved Jack. Jack shoved back. They shouldered and butted till they went sprawling in the leaves. Then like two grizzly bears, the fur really began to fly, or rather the leaves were flying. Jack and Billy writhed and squirmed in the mountain of leaves. At times, they were so submerged that all that could be seen was the pile of leaves being buffeted around like a walking haystack. Then they would surface, spin around, and flop back onto the pile.

"Get him, Jack, get him," shouted the kids.

Something told Billy that he'd better scram out of there. Billy felt Jack had too many things on his side. For one thing, everyone was cheering for Jack, and that meant the kids believed Jack was right. And, second, they were fighting in Jack's yard, and that made Billy feel a little uneasy. It also seemed to give Jack a fighting advantage. So Billy left, calling back a few insults as he walked away. Both boys were ruffled and snarled with leaves, but otherwise unhurt.

Just as Jack was beginning to feel pretty good about his tussle with Billy, who should drive in? Mr. Holiday! His eyes nearly fell out when he saw how the pile of leaves in the yard had mushroomed. The second he'd garaged the car, he marched to the front lawn to make certain his eyes weren't playing tricks on him. He was dumbfounded to find that the yard was heaping with loads more leaves than when he left it. It was a tense moment – so quiet you could have heard a leaf drop.

"Where the devil did all this come from?" asked Mr. Holiday.

He looked at each in turn. And the picture he saw, was a bunch of wrinkled ragamuffins all snarled with leaves stuck to their hair, sweaters, cuffs, and collars.

"Gee, Dad. We were just making something," said Jack.

"You can just haul this mess out back… and be quick about it!"

Mr. Holiday was seldom angry, but when he was, it was obvious to all. The pyramid builders somberly set to work. Soon, the neighborhood members of the work crew drifted away, giving one excuse or another, leaving Jack, Nancy, and Peedie to finish their assigned chore. The three worked in grumpy silence, each in their own mind blaming the others for the mess.

Before the job was finished, however, Mr. Holiday came outside and helped them. His temper seemed to have cooled. Perhaps he took pity on the kids because of the size of the job. Or maybe he remembered a time when leaves were not just a nuisance, but were fun for jumping in, too.

CHAPTER VIII

# The Haunted Halloween

For weeks, Jack had thought about what to wear on Halloween. Other years, he'd dressed as a clown or a hobo. This year he hoped to think of something different. He wanted to make an original costume. All the stores were featuring Halloween things, and Jack had wandered through many of them looking for ideas. Peedie had already decided he wanted to be Superman. And Nancy planned to dress as a witch. But Jack couldn't come up with anything.

"What are you going to be on Halloween, Jack?" Benjie had asked.

"I'm not going to tell. I want it to be a surprise."

Of course, Jack didn't even know himself what he was going to be, but he hadn't said that. The more secretive it seemed, the more everyone teased to find out how he was going to dress up. Halloween came and Jack still hadn't worked up his costume. Down the street, Billy Suggs met Arthur, who was delivering his newspapers:

"Hi Artie. Are you going tricks or treating tonight?"

"Sure I are. I might take two tricks or treats bags."

"Two?"

"Yeah. A paper one and maybe my newspaper bag."

"How about going around ringing doorbells with me?"

"Okay. I hadn't made no plans yet, neither."

Billy and Arthur walked along awhile not speaking. Billy, his head down, watched the leaves flutter up as his toe kicked them. His hands were deep in his pockets, and deep were his thoughts. Suddenly, and quite unexpectedly, he said:

"You want to play a trick on Jack Holiday?"

In his eye, Billy had a devilish glint, and he was nodding his head coaxingly.

"What you got in mind?"

"Just a sort of surprise. You go see Jack and tell him to meet you tonight over at the old haunted house."

"The haunted house?" Arthur's eyes bulged out.

The haunted house was a deserted house on Dobbins Street. Since it was old and vandalized and next to the cemetery, it had earned the name of being haunted from the kids in town.

"What's the matter? You're not afraid of going there, are you?" asked Billy.

Arthur didn't answer Billy right off. If Arthur heard a bump in the night, first thing he thought of was ghosts. He guessed that ghosts always hid in the dark. And so he was always ready to jump out of his skin if he had to walk alone in dark places. Of course, he had never met a ghost face to face. He took special pains not to. If it ever

51

happened that he met up with a ghost, Arthur just knew what he'd do – he'd made plans ahead. If he couldn't run, rather than fight, he'd join 'em. One time it was dark, and he had a hunch there was a ghost nearby and he called out:

"Don't scare me, I are on your side."

"What about it, huh?"

"What do you want Jack to meet us at the old haunted house for, Billy? Can't he meet us someplace else?"

"No. That'd spoil it. I got a plan to play a joke on him, see? Just to sort of scare him. So, come on Artie. Be a sport. What are you afraid of, Jack or the haunted house?"

"Maybe he won't come. Maybe I can't talk him into it."

"You can talk him into it, Artie, if you try. Remember though, don't mention my name. Let that be a surprise, too."

As scared as Arthur was of ghosts, he was also as workable as putty. And it wasn't long before Billy had talked him into it. They made their plans. Arthur was to ask Jack to meet him at the haunted house at nine o'clock. After supper, Billy and Arthur would go tricks or treating, then go to Dobbins Street and hide on Jack.

Halloween evening came. A big bright Jack-O-lantern moon peeked through the skeleton fingers of the leafless trees. There was a rustling and a smell of burnt leaves. And the wind had a frosty nip to it. A Halloween parade was held uptown. And afterward, there were refreshments of cider and donuts in the park. Then the kids, like little haunts, went house to house ringing bells. They pranced out of the shadows and into the porch-lit circles – holding up sacks to collect their treats. The masqueraders had faces daubed with colors or hidden behind masks. Some wore half masks and costumes of storyland. Others had on full masks with big eyes and noses and mouths. And still more had on scary masks – ghouls and skulls and Frankensteins.

"Who could you be?" said Mr. Yeager. The kids had just rung his doorbell and shouted, "Tricks or treats!"

"Is that witch Mary Jane?"

Nancy giggled. "No, Mary Jane is dressed like a bride. I'm Nancy."

"Oh, it's you, Nancy. I couldn't tell."

Peedie stepped forward in his Superman suit to get his treat, followed by Benjie as an Indian, Alvin as a robot, and Donald as Popeye. Getting their treats, they moved on to be followed by more bell ringers. Fifteen minutes later, Billy and Arthur rang the bell.

Mr. Yeager dropped treats into each of their sacks. Billy was dressed like a pirate, and Arthur was dressed like the devil. Mr. Yeager peered over his spectacles. "I recognize you, Billy. But who's the devil with you?"

Arthur snickered. "Can't you guess who I are?"

"Oh, it's you, Arthur."

"How did you knowed it was me?"

"Just a good guess." Billy thanked Mr. Yeager as he and Arthur left. After they walked away from the house, Billy lifted his mask and looked inside his tricks or treat bag.

"I got a candy bar," said Billy. "What'd you get, Artie?"

"I got a popcorn ball."

"Let's finish going to the houses on this side of the street, then it'll be about nine o'clock and time to meet Jack at the haunted house."

Billy and Arthur stopped at every house with a lighted porchlight, or where friends told them there were treats. On their way down the street, they met school friends whom they couldn't recognize with their masks on. Finally, they came to the end of the street, rang the bell, and collected their last treat.

"What'd you get this time, Artie?" asked Billy.

"Oh, geez!" said Arthur, slapping himself in the head. "They done it again. They give me another popcorn ball!"

Billy laughed. "They sure know a cornball when they see one coming. Come on, we got to get to Dobbins Street before Jack gets there."

The stars were shining, and the leaves rustled across their path and swirled around their feet. They heard the quiet that only a cemetery makes, sitting behind its rusted iron fence. Away off, they could hear a dog howling warnings. The moon was lighting the gravestones to where Arthur couldn't look. It made him cold and scared and shivery.

"I didn't bring nothing to keep the bad luck off of me, Billy. This street gives me the goose pimples. What is we coming here for anyways?"

"Just to play a joke. You're sure Jack said he'd meet you here like you asked him to?" Billy was walking along pretty fast, but Arthur was making sure he kept up with him. The air seemed much cooler, and a rising mist haloed the street lamp.

"Do you believe in ghosts, Billy? I mean, there must be something to it, or why would big folks talk about 'em?"

"Don't be a scaredy cat, Artie. I've been over to that house lots of times and I've never seen any ghosts."

"Does not seeing none prove there ain't any?"

"Well, does not seeing any prove there *is*? Look, I'll go ahead first and you can follow me if that's what's bothering you."

At the end of the cemetery stood the house. It was all angles and sagging and damp-looking as a fog rose around it.

In the yard was a jungle of decayed weeds and tangled clumps and rotting fallen limbs. The curtain-less, busted-out windows of the house were like dark, hollow eye sockets staring out at them.

"L-let's go, Billy. What if Jack forget what I told him. Then what?"

"Then it might go bad for you!"

"Don't say that, Billy."

"Shooosh!"

"Was that you that done that, Billy? You hear something?"

"Yes, you? Be quiet, Artie, and stop shaking your popcorn balls. You'll tip off Jack that we're here and spoil everything."

"I can't help shaking, can I? Besides, I think it's spoiled already. It's spoiled for me, anyhow."

The boys went tiptoeing through the yard. The rotting leaves were soggy under their feet. Now and then, a brittle weed stalk would crunch. When they got close to the house it smelled musty, like a breath from the house itself.

"Yipe!"

"What's the matter?" asked Billy, turning around to Arthur.

"Something's got me, Billy. Help!"

Billy could see that Arthur was tugging like he was going to die if he couldn't get loose. Then something went r-r-r-rip!

"Oh, a spook is got me! I just know it."

"Hold still, Artie, I'll fix it. It's only the tail of your devil suit that's got caught on some prickers."

"Whew!" said Arthur, after Billy had freed him from the pricker bush. "I thought I was a goner sure."

"Keep your voice down, Artie, and try to be more careful this time. Jack might be along any minute and we don't want to scare him away before he comes up to the house. Pick up your back and watch where you're going."

They listened some more and squinched their eyes to see into the shadows. The rain gutters of the house were draped like frazzled curtain hems. The porch railings had gaps like broken teeth. Billy looked back to Arthur and waved him on. Arthur's legs were saying run, but his head was telling him that it was better to stick with Billy than go it alone. They reached the porch. They were close enough to see the spiders in the windows.

"We ain't going in there, is we?" Arthur's eyes were dancing side to side like two nervous marbles.

"Sure, we're going in there. What do you think we came here for?"

"I dunno, and I sure wish it weren't me here to find out."

They tiptoed onto the porch. The boards creaked and they could feel them sag under their weight. Their feet rasped on the gritty, dirty, dust laden boards. The cobwebs they broke through made them feel all itchy and spidery.

"I don't like this. Ain't you ever heard of vampires?"

"Sh-h-h! We're almost inside."

"Inside? Man, oh man! What'd I go and listen to you for? You gotta be crazy going in there. This is some joke, I'll say."

Arthur had gone too far to turn back and he was almost too petrified to move forward. The top of his tricks and treat sack was limp from his sweaty grip.

"Like I said, all you've got to do is follow me."

"Okay, but let me stay near."

Billy and Arthur were creeping towards the door when it happened. Billy saw it first and didn't stick around long enough to make out what it was. All he knew was that something white was standing in the doorway – and it moved! Arthur was so close to Billy that when Billy jumped back, he knocked Arthur head for heels. Falling back, Arthur sat flat on his tricks or treat bag, squashing his popcorn balls.

Billy went tearing off, bouncing through clumps of bushes with all the running speed his legs could gather. Arthur didn't need to be told what to do. He flew to his feet. Billy was no slouch of a runner, but Artie quickly sped off, overtook and passed him. They didn't stop till they were out of Dobbins Street and out of breath, too.

"What-what-what-was that, anyhow?" panted Billy.

"Whew! Don't ask me. I are glad to be away from that spooky joint. And I'll tell you another thing," said Arthur, looking warily back over his shoulder.

"What-what's that?"

"I are never going back to find out what it was, neither."

Was there a ghost on Dobbins Street? As it turns out, they never did go back to the haunted house to find out what Billy had seen. When Arthur got home and got his wind back, he was pretty unhappy about losing all his trick or treats. He had dropped his bag when he ran. Nonetheless, he also thought that it was a small price to pay for saving his skin.

Meanwhile, Jack had said goodnight to Benjie and was walking home by himself, his white sheet dragging on the ground.

"Why," he wondered, "had Artie run off? Also, who was with him?" Jack was sorry that he didn't have a chance to show off his scary new ghost costume.

## CHAPTER IX

# Arguments and Armistice

A wall of grey light rose out of the East. It was a bleak November morning, drizzling and chilly. The autumn leaves seemed pasted to the damp pavement. Peedie, Jack, and Benjie pattered up the shiny sidewalk toward the school door.

It was one of those dreary mornings that makes one stop and think. And Jack had a lot to think about. Jack was puzzled over what had happened Halloween night. He wondered who had come up to the old haunted house, and then ran away so fast. All he was sure of, was that there were two of them. And whoever they were, Benjie had the same questions in his mind when he looked at Jack and said:

"Who do you think it could have been, Jack?"

"I don't know. It was too dark to make out."

Peedie was skipping alongside his big brother, listening to him talk with Benjie.

"Wish I'd been there with my Superman suit," said Peedie. "I could have seen 'em with my x-ray eyes."

"Don't be funny, Peedie," said Jack. "We're trying to figure this out."

"Do you think it was Artie?" Said Benjie, looking solemn.

"That's what's so mysterious. Why would Artie ask me to meet him there and then run away? That's what I can't figure out."

Benjie suddenly brightened, rubbed his hands together and smiled. "Whoever it was, one of them was in such a big hurry, he dropped his tricks or treat bag."

"Yeah," said Jack. "But who wants mashed popcorn balls?"

Peedie skipped on ahead and did a flip around a pipe rail by the school door.

"How will we ever find out who it was?" said Benjie.

"I'm not sure yet, but I'm going to ask Artie about it today in school."

"Okay. See you after school, Jack," said Benjie

As the boys separated inside the school corridor, Jack waved goodbye to Benjie and Peedie and went to his own classroom locker to hang up his coat. Children were streaming toward the school like spokes to a hub. Hallways and rooms were just coming to life while Jack's thoughts were full of what had happened the night before at the old house on Dobbins street. He was eager to hear what Arthur would have to say about it. Jack didn't know that talk of a ghost at the old haunted house was already spreading throughout the school. Seeing a ghost was, that very minute, making Billy and Arthur famous. The more kids asked about the ghost, the more Billy puffed up and their story stretched out.

When Jack entered the classroom, the first thing he noticed was a cluster of kids around Artie and Billy. The 8:50 bell hadn't rung yet. Kids were crowded around the pair, pressing them with questions. Billy was leaning back in his chair, and Arthur was sitting on the desk just behind him. Fred had just asked:

"Are you sure it was a ghost?"

"You know I never believed in ghosts before," said Billy. "So, when I say I saw a ghost, you can be sure that it's a fact."

"What'd it look like?"

"M-m, it was big and white and misty. Isn't that right, Artie?"

"Sure, it are." Arthur had missed seeing the ghost because Billy had barreled him over in his rush to escape. But Arthur wasn't about to say that. It'd be like saying he'd been at the Great Chicago Fire and had seen no flames. Besides, the way Billy was telling the story made it so real that Arthur was half convinced that he'd seen it himself.

The kids listened to Billy's every word. Their mouths were gaping and their eyes were full of wonder, all except Jack who listened closely, but had a strange kind of tilt to his head.

"Did it touch you?" asked Mary Jane with a shiver.

"Not exactly, but I could tell it could pass through walls and things. Isn't that so, Artie?"

"It sure are."

"Did you see it pass through walls?" asked Rodney.

"No, but I could tell it could. Couldn't you, Artie? See, even Artie could tell. It was about nine o'clock and Artie and I sneaked up on the porch. It was real dark. We were just almost in the door before I saw it. When I came face to face with it, I just looked it in the eye."

As Billy told about meeting the ghost, he took on a fierce look. The horror of meeting a ghost eye to eye made the girls shudder and swoon over Billy's bravery. Billy was getting a lot of attention from the girls, but it was Jennifer's attention that bothered Jack the most. She in particular, or so it seemed to Jack, was sighing and throwing admiring glances at Billy. Jack wanted to show up Billy's ghost for bunk, but his curiosity to hear more stopped him.

"Golly," said Fred. "Did you say it had an eye?"

"Well, it was too dark to see, you understand."

"Did you actually touch it?" asked Jennifer.

"Just a little. Didn't I, Artie?"

Arthur was nodding and grinning ear to ear. He was enjoying the story just as much as the others. Jack was becoming more annoyed by all the attention Billy was getting from Jennifer.

"What did it feel like?" said Jennifer.

"Kind of like it was there and yet, not there, if you get what I mean." Everybody seemed to understand and looked serious. Jack folded his arms and began to tap his foot.

"What did you do after that, Billy?"

Billy looked back over his shoulder at Arthur.

"Why, you dummy! You were there. Don't you remember? After I touched it, it disappeared."

"Oh yeah, yeah, yeah. I forget."

Jack stifled a little chuckle with his hand. "Don't you mean *you* disappeared?" he laughed.

Billy threw a quizzical scowl at Jack.

"Why, Jack. What a thing to say," said Jennifer. "After Billy braved death going to that haunted house and facing that – ghost."

To be frowned upon by Jennifer was not what Jack had counted on. He had no wish to argue with her over whether Billy had seen a ghost or not. And yet, somehow, he found himself placed in just that very embarrassing position. The strain of it played across his face and tied his tongue. Jack felt, somehow, he must convince them now that there really wasn't any ghost.

"Just what did you mean by that crack about us disappearing?" said Billy, getting ready for battle with all the righteousness of someone wronged.

With everyone frowning at him including Jennifer, things looked black for Jack. Then it came to him that the truth was on his side. Jack knew that Billy had not seen a ghost, and that he had run away. The only thing that Jack didn't figure on was that when someone backs a lie, he'll usually stand up for it and fight, because nobody likes to be proved wrong, even when he is.

"I'll tell you why I said you disappeared. I saw you run – you and Artie. Why, you were so scared, you knocked Artie down trying to get away. Isn't that right, Artie?"

At these words, Billy turned white – almost as white as the ghost he'd thought he'd seen. It was his turn to stammer. He'd built up a false framework and didn't have a leg to stand on. That meant he had to do some patching up, or fall flat on his face.

"Oh, so you were back somewhere safely hidden, chicken. I knew you were too yellow to meet us at the haunted house."

"Who you calling yellow and a chicken?" Jack thrust his shoulders forward and Billy stood up.

"You, that's who. If you hadn't been afraid to go in the haunted house, you would have seen the ghost like we did, wouldn't he, Artie?"

Poor Artie's head was spinning. First, he was agreeing with Jack and then he was agreeing with Billy.

The argument was getting noisy. Some of the children looked nervously toward Ms. Rivera working at her desk at the front of the room. Billy was gritting his teeth, ready to fight. Jack was equally determined to convince Jennifer that *he* was right. Now he would settle for nothing less than winning the argument. What's more, he was steamed up enough to win and gloat over it.

"What do you mean?" said Jack, looking Billy squarely in the face, "Saying I didn't have the guts enough to see the ghost. It was *me* you saw. I *was* the ghost! That's how I dressed for Halloween."

Billy got whiter than before. But like a goat with its horns locked, there was no face-saving way out, but to keep on butting.

"You're a liar! You're just making that up. You've got no proof, but *I* do. Artie was there and saw it, too."

"So? I got a witness. Benjie was with me. Besides, Artie knows you ran. Didn't he run, Artie?"

Before Artie could answer, the teacher grabbed the back of his collar and led him to his seat.

"Didn't you hear the bell? It's time to start school. Furthermore, we'll have no fighting in school."

Except for the two glaring at each other, the fight fizzled out. It always seemed to Jack that whenever a good and serious discussion was going on, school interfered with it. There was a deep hush in the room, as Ms. Rivera took attendance. After the Pledge of Allegiance, Ms. Rivera stood at the front of the room next to the flag.

"There is no school November 11th. I wonder if any of you know why. Do you know what day that is?"

Mary Jane raised her hand. And Ms. Rivera called on her.

"Isn't it Veteran's Day?"

"That's correct, Mary Jane. Veterans Day, or Armistice Day, as it used to be called. Now, how many of you think you could tell the class anything about what Veteran's Day stands for?"

The children did a lot of looking around at each other in the class, while Ms. Rivera looked for a volunteer.

Arthur raised his hand.

"Yes, Arthur."

"I forget about Veterans Day, but I think Armistice Day is when trees is planted."

"Trees? No, Arthur. I think you have confused Armistice Day with Arbor Day. Arbor Day is when we plant a tree."

"See, I knowed it," said Arthur.

"Knowed what? I mean *knew* what, Arthur?" asked Ms. Rivera.

"I knewed I had 'em mixed up."

"Thank you, Arthur. Anyone else know what Veteran's Day stands for? All right, I guess I'll have to call on you, Mary Jane."

"Wasn't it the end of World War I?"

"Yes. At 11o'clock on the morning of November 11, 1918. You know what a truce is don't you, children? A truce is when both sides agree to stop fighting. When the armistice was signed between Germany and the Allies, the guns of the four-year war were silenced. Our president then was Woodrow Wilson. He called it 'a war to end all wars'. But, as you know, World War I was followed by World War II. So, on June 1st, 1954, Congress changed the name from Armistice Day to Veteran's Day. The day was dedicated to world peace.

Ms. Rivera called on Jennifer who had a question.

"Won't there ever be an end to wars?" she asked.

"Jennifer, let's hope that someday there will be an end to war. Maybe someday people will understand more about what causes war. I hope that Veteran's Day will give you a chance to think about that."

During the day, there was an armistice between Billy and Jack. Not that they didn't continue to glare at on another, but generally they were watched closely. And, besides, they were too busy to battle anymore. They had discovered that even the most exciting fight grows tiresome carried on too long.

So the argument was left like so many other things in life – never fully settled. Jack knew that he was right. And Billy knew that Jack was right. But Billy wasn't able to admit being wrong without losing face. And poor Artie, never able to change his mind about anything, still believed there was a ghost at the old house on Dobbins Street.

## CHAPTER X

# Cold Turkey Thanksgiving

When Thanksgiving rolled around, Jack was resigned to sticking close to home. Not only was it expected of him, it was expected of his friends as well, so there was little point in trying to arrange any neighborhood activity. Jack loafed around the house, while Nancy helped mother in the kitchen.

"How many places should I set at the table?" Nancy asked, as she reached into the dish cupboard for plates.

"Let's see," said Mrs. Holiday. "There's Peedie, Jack, and Dad, and you and I make five. Then there'll be Aunt Lulu, Uncle Ollie, and Grampa. That's eight, all together." Mrs. Holiday looked in the oven and basted the turkey.

"There's one more," said Nancy.

"Oh, who did I leave out?"

"Butterball."

"Oh, yes. Mustn't forget the cat on Thanksgiving. As if anyone could forget Butterball. He's always underfoot anyway."

Nancy counted out eight plates. Then the cat followed her out to the dining room, as she set the table.

"Mom, how are Aunt Lulu and Uncle Ollie related to us?"

"Well, Nancy, Uncle Ollie is my big brother, just like Jack is your big brother."

"You mean you grew up together in the same house?"

"That's right. Is that hard to believe?"

Nancy thought a minute and then said:

"Did you ever fight?"

"You mean like you and Jack? Yes, we had our squabbles. I guess all brothers and sisters do. But most of the time we got along pretty well."

Twenty minutes later, Aunt Lulu and Uncle Ollie drove in, bringing Grandfather with them. Aunt Lulu gave each of the kids a big hug. Peedie was careful to stay clear of her prickly brooch. Then Aunt Lulu put on an apron and helped Nancy and Mrs. Holiday in the kitchen. Soon, all the family was sitting in the dining room. The table was spread with dishes heaped with mashed potatoes, turkey dressing, cranberry sauce, cabbage salad, squash, and peas and carrots. Then Mr. Holiday carved the golden-brown turkey. Butterball mewed, paced back and forth, or sometimes sat and licked his whiskers. Aunt Lulu said grace, and the meal began.

Later, after everyone had stuffed themselves, slices of pumpkin pie or apple pie with pieces of cheese were served. Coffee was poured for the grownups and milk for the children.

"Sure you won't have another slice of pumpkin pie, Ollie?" asked Mrs. Holiday.

"No more for me, thanks. I'm stuffed," said Uncle Ollie, leaning back from the table and patting his vest. "You know, I can't eat a Thanksgiving dinner without having that other Thanksgiving come to mind. Remember it, Dorothy? The 'cold turkey' Thanksgiving?"

"Oh! I'm sure I'll never forget that one, even thought I was pretty young at the time," said Mrs. Holiday.

"You must have been about eight, because I think I'd just turned twelve. You haven't forgotten about it – have you, Dad?" Oliver said to Grandfather Claggett across the table.

Grandfather smiled wryly and lit his pipe.

"Tell us about it, Uncle Ollie," said Jack who, next to dreaming up ideas, always liked to listen to a good story.

"Jack, I suppose it's difficult to imagine that Thanksgivings were a little different back in the days when your mom and I were kids. For one thing, we didn't have television or supermarkets. And mostly it was a quiet day – a day of good food and rest. Somehow you were closer to things then, too. For instance, instead of picking out a turkey from the freezer chest at the supermarket, we'd go to the farm and pick out the bird as it was strutting around.

"But, as I was saying, it was the Thanksgiving where we had cold turkey that I'll never forget. We had a pet cat, too. Only it wasn't orange like yours, Nancy. It was a black and white striped tiger cat. We named it Lily. I know, it was a bad joke – tiger lily – but for all that, it was a pretty good pet.

"Your mom loved that cat. Remember, Dorothy, how you used to dress it up in little doll clothes? Especially that bonnet and night gown. That was too much. One time, I swear, the poor cat got a look at itself in the mirror and was so ashamed, it hid out under the barn for two days."

"Nancy dresses Butterball like that, sometimes," smiled Peedie through his missing baby teeth.

"Butterball is a live wire, compared to your mother's cat back when we were kids, Peedie. Her cat must have had some night life, because she slept most all day. It'd stretch out on the carpet and look for all the world like it was dead. Even when it did move – was it slow! My God, that cat was slow. If you can imagine an over-size beanbag on legs, you can get some notion of the sluggishness of Lily. In a race against a snail, I would have bet on the snail. As a matter of fact, I never did see that cat move, except for that one Thanksgiving. But I'm getting ahead of my story.

"Our Thanksgivings were always big family affairs. All the preparation that went into getting up that dinner, you wouldn't believe it. For all the time spent on it, there should have been enough to feed George Washington's army. As a matter of fact, I'll bet it didn't fall short by much. Mother used to fret so much over that dinner – you remember, Dorothy, how she used to fret? Why, it was enough to make *you* tired. That's why your grandfather, here, used to stay clear of the kitchen."

Mr. Claggett smiled through a puff of pipe smoke.

"At that time, Uncle Harry was living with us. I can remember him just as plain as anything, snoozing in the big overstuffed mohair chair in the dining room. Nobody slept more than Great Uncle Harry, except maybe the cat. I don't know why that chair was in the dining room, but I *do* know that man never missed a meal.

"Uncle Harry had some terrific memories to tell – all about his early pioneering days and Indian raids and such. Sometimes he'd show me his shotgun that he still kept in the hall closet. He'd often dream about Indian raiding parties coming after his scalp. Why he worried about being scalped, I don't know. The top of his head was as smooth as a bowling ball. Nothing for any self-respecting Indian to get hold of. Anyway, he'd have these Indian nightmares.

"Then there was Cousin Agnes. Now there was a nervous woman. She couldn't face the day without a dose of her nerve medicine. She bought it by the case. She was helping Mother with the Thanksgiving fixings that day. I can still remember Mother shooing me out of the kitchen. Remember that, Dorothy? You were helping with the dinner, and I was poking around, getting in Cousin Agnes' way. She was the jumpiest woman. The least thing would upset her. Remember her?"

"Oh, I remember her all right," said Mrs. Holiday. "But there were so many there that Thanksgiving, I don't think I remember them all."

"Do you remember Widow Dumphy? Ma invited her so she wouldn't have to spend the holiday alone. Now there was a proud woman. I'll never forget those hats she used to wear. It made her look something like Robin Hood in black with those two big pheasant feathers sticking up out of the top of her hat." Uncle Oliver took a sip of coffee.

"There we all were, getting ready for a big Thanksgiving dinner. Your mother and I were about the same age as you and Nancy are right now. And you want to know a funny thing? It was your grandfather here who started the whole thing off."

"Well, I don't know about that," said Grandfather, tapping his pipe on the ash tray. "I think Widow Dumphy started it all off."

"I always thought it was Cousin Agnes," said Mrs. Holiday.

"That just goes to show how jumbled things were that day, because Agnes blamed it all on the cat," said Uncle Oliver.

"Lord, it was a puzzle."

"What did happen?" asked Jack.

"Let me see if I can reconstruct the whole thing," said Uncle Oliver, sipping more coffee. "It started out with your grandfather sitting in the living room in his favorite rocking chair, reading. Lily, the tiger-striped cat, was peacefully stretched out at his feet, asleep. And not to be outdone by any old cat, Great Uncle Harry was fast asleep in the dining room in his big overstuffed chair."

"Ahem, it all really started," said Grandfather, clearing his throat, "when Widow Dumphy came to the front door and rang the bell. Because that's when I rocked forward. I was getting up to answer the doorbell."

"Well, that's true enough," said Uncle Oliver. "From the minute you rocked forward in your chair, you set the whole thing in motion."

"Yes," agreed Mrs. Holiday. "But if Cousin Agnes hadn't been carrying a dish of cranberry sauce from the kitchen into the dining room just at that minute, the whole thing might never have happened."

"I don't get it, Uncle Ollie."

"Jack, the minute your Grandfather rocked forward in order to answer the doorbell, the rocker of his chair landed on poor old sleeping Lily's tail. You never saw such action out of a cat in all your life. That cat tore off like her tail was afire, as most likely it was after it got pinched under the rocker. And not being the least discriminating, that cat made straight for Cousin Agnes. True, she was about as straight up and down as a tree. The minute that cat leaped on her skirt, she nearly jumped out of her skin. She couldn't help it. She was a nervous woman. She let out a blood-curdling scream and let fly the dish of cranberry sauce.

66

"The dish of cranberry sauce bounced off Uncle Harry's bald head. Of course, he woke up. But being beaned with the dish of cranberry, he must have woke-up in a real daze. When he sprang to his feet – for an old man he was pretty nimble – first thing he must have seen when he jumped up was his own reflection in the buffet mirror. With the red cranberry juice running down his face, he must have thought that he was being scalped - for he bellowed out: "Injuns! Run for your lives!" Next thing we knew, he was in the hall closet and had hauled out his shotgun. Well, we all ran for cover. Just then, Widow Dumphy, who had been waiting at the front door, decided to let herself in and opened the door. She was to repent of that decision long after. For the minute Uncle Harry saw that door opening and got a look at those feathers sticking out of her hat, he must have mistook her for the last of the Mohicans, for he let fire with a blast from his shotgun that shook the whole house."

"Did she get shot?"

"No, Nancy. Luckily, the shot missed Widow Dumphy. Either the widow fainted, or your Great Uncle was an awful lousy shot. Now that I think about it, if it had ended there, it might never have made the newspaper."

"It was in the newspaper?" asked Jack.

"Front page. You see, though the shot missed the widow, as luck would have it, the blast shot the tires off a passing automobile. It was a Model T Ford driven by Reverend Tweekle, the Baptist minister, and it caused him to swerve his machine into a ditch. From what I heard later, it scared the wits out of his reverence. I do remember it caused him to invoke a few blessings off the cuff, so to speak."

"How did it all end, Uncle Ollie?"

"Well, Cousin Agnes got out her nerve medicine – a whole quart of the stuff, and got a good dose down herself, and Widow Dumphy, and Uncle Harry, too, after they were able to disarm him and get him pinned down on the floor."

"What happened to the minister?" asked Jack.

"Reverend Tweekle? He left his car in the ditch and crawled on his hands and knees till he was out of firing range, and went for the sheriff. Later, the sheriff and his deputies, all heavily armed, came up to our house. Your grandfather here answered the door and tried to explain the whole improbable mess. He might just as well have made up a story, for they didn't believe the one you told them, did they, Dad?"

"Wasn't that so much," said Grandfather, clicking his pipe stem against his dental plate. "It was Agnes' nerve medicine they got a whiff of."

"Oh, was that it?" said Oliver. "I didn't remember that. But I *do* remember the sheriff's men taking them away like three desperadoes. Kids, your mother was so worried, she cried and cried."

"I was scared I might never see them again," said Mrs. Holiday.

"Were they put in jail?" asked Nancy.

"No. Your grandfather arranged bail. And much later, we were able to sit down to a Thanksgiving dinner of cold turkey. As I remember, Widow Dumphy refused to sit down and couldn't be talked into staying. I guess. Although she hadn't been hit by buckshot, her vanity had been wounded by having her picture taken wearing her new hat with the feathers shot off and all. When the picture appeared in the paper the next day, they did look every bit like fugitives from a chain gang. I don't think the widow ever forgave Uncle Harry.

"Despite the cold turkey, I remember Mother found something to be thankful for that day. If there was the slightest excuse for thankfulness, she'd seek it out. Remember, Dad, her saying that she was glad that Harry hadn't shot the tires off *our* minister's car? If he had, she would have been so ashamed – so embarrassed – she'd probably have had to quit the church.

CHAPTER XI

# Football Plays and Pileups

For weeks and weeks and weeks, Jack would look forward to a vacation from school. He'd yearn for it, dream of it. He'd count off the days. Monday through Friday, he'd watch the calendar days peel away leading up to it. Then, when it finally did come, he was never really ready for it. He had nothing planned.

Thanksgiving vacation was like that. Thursday had taken care of itself, of course, what with relatives visiting and the turkey and all. Now it was Friday morning and Jack stayed in bed thinking. He could hear the TV downstairs. Peedie was probably watching cartoons. Jack wondered if Nancy was up yet.

"Turn that down, I want to sleep!" Nancy shouted down the stairs.

Jack smiled to himself. No, Nancy wasn't up yet either. Nancy liked to sleep late in the morning more than anyone else in the family, but she got very crabby because Peedie would turn on the cartoons early and wake her up anyway.

Jack lay in bed with his hands folded under his head looking at the ceiling, thinking. It was wonderful not to have to get up and rush to school. Ah, the freedom of it. It made Jack feel tingly and fine. But freedom always brought the problem of how to use it and what to do with it. Maybe he could start that clubhouse he'd always dreamed of building. But how? He didn't have any lumber or anyplace to build. Or maybe he could pack a lunch and go exploring. But where? It was always a problem what to make, where to go, and what to do. Maybe it would be better to get up a football game over in the field. Sure, why not, he thought. Jack had watched the last part of the big Cotton Bowl game on television and had gotten some new ideas he wanted to try.

He jumped out of bed, dressed, and put on a couple of sweatshirts. Then he galumphed down the stairs. Peedie was too interested in the television to notice him pass through the living room into the kitchen. Jack poured himself a heaping bowl of cornflakes and then read what was printed on the cereal box while he spooned them down.

"Good morning, Jack," said Mother. Did you have some juice?"

"Hi, Mom. No, I didn't yet," said Jack.

Mrs. Holiday reached in the cupboard, brought out a glass and poured Jack a glass of Welch's grape juice. "I want you to take the waste baskets out and dump the papers before you do anything else this morning." Jack nodded, his cheeks puffed up with crunchy corn flakes. "By the way, Jack, what do you plan to do today?"

"I'm hoping to get up a football game over in the field."

"Not with those good trousers on, you're not. Don't forget to change into some old jeans before you go over to play football."

"Aw, Mom, these pants look neat."

"I know it. And that's why you're not going to play football in them. I want you to keep them looking neat."

"Did I hear someone say football?" It was Peedie. He could be deep in the middle of a Mickey Mouse cartoon, and still not miss a thing that was said anywhere in the house.

"Forget it, Peedie. I wasn't talking to you," said Jack, tipping his dish to get the last spoonful.

"I thought I heard the word 'football,'" said Peedie.

"Go back to your TV. You're missing Mickey."

"Didn't you say football?" said Peedie. I could have sworn I heard you say football."

"You must be hearing things, Peedie."

Peedie kept eyeing Jack's football sweater suspiciously.

Mrs. Holiday felt she'd waited long enough for the matter to settle itself. "Jack, is there any reason why Peedie can't play with you?"

"Yes, Mom. He's too little. Can you imagine Peedie tackling Benjie or Billie or Artie, or even Rodney" Why, he couldn't even tackle Mary Jane." Jack felt that that clinched the argument.

"Bet I could, too, tackle Mary Jane," said Peedie.

"Aren't there other things he can do?" said Mrs. Holiday.

"Like what, Mom?"

"Couldn't he pass the football?"

"Mom, did you ever see Peedie pass the ball? He can hardly throw it past his own foot."

"I can, too," said Peedie.

"I meant that Peedie could pass at the line," said Mrs. Holiday.

"You mean hike it?" said Jack, frowning. "Can't you see Peedie being the center on a line drive? Some interference *he'd* run. He'd be trampled down like an ant."

"I think you ought to be able to figure out something so Peedie can play. You were small once, you know."

"Okay, Mom. But don't blame me if he comes home bawling."

"I don't bawl," said Peedie.

It wasn't long before Jack and Peedie were heading toward Benjie's house. It was a mild Friday for November. A few soft sunbeams slanted through the clouds. A little northeasterly breeze rippled the trees, and in the evergreens, some sparrows chattered.

"Hi Benjie. Would you like to play some football?"

"Sure, Jack," said Benjie rubbing his hands. "Who else is going to play?"

"Well, I called Artie and he's going to stop over for Billy Suggs and round up whoever else he can."

"Where's your football?" asked Benjie.

"Worn out. Can't we use yours?"

"Mine's shot, too."

"Darn! I was planning on us using it."

"Oh, didn't I tell you, Jack? I was playing catch with my sister, Ellen, and – you know she can't catch – well, the Wilson's dog ..."

"Dusty?"

"Yeah, Dusty. He caught my football instead of my sister."

"Then what?"

"You didn't expect he would throw it back did you?"

"No, of course not. But what happened to it then?"

"He ate it."

"Your football? No kidding. Did he swallow it?"

"No, but he chewed it up. So, ...," Benjie shrugged his shoulders.

"So that was the end of your football."

"Then where are we going to get a football, Jack?" asked Peedie.

"Where else. We'll have to ask Rodney to play."

Rodney Van Skotus had more toys and sports stuff than any boy on the block. The boys didn't like having Rodney in the game, because if Rodney got bumped or even mussed a little bit, his mother would complain to Jack or Benjie's mother, and that would sometimes break up the whole game. But like many other things, the boys decided they had to risk it. It was Rodney – or no game at all.

Jack rang the bell and Rodney's mother answered the door.

"Come in, boys," she said. 'The boys are here to see you, dear."

Rodney came to the door licking a peppermint stick. Jack wasn't sure he could get Rodney to play. Rodney could sometimes be stubborn as a mule. But this time, it didn't take long to get him to agree. It took him much longer to get dressed for the game. He had to pass his mother's inspection. When Jack, Peedie, Benjie, and Rodney did reach the field, they found the rest of the boys already there waiting. All the boys were bigger than Peedie.

"Peedie, are you sure you don't want to change your mind?" said Jack. "We're playing tackle, you know."

"No, I want to play," said Peedie.

"I hope you don't go bawling home to Mom."

Rodney was the only boy with a complete football uniform. The rest might have one item like a helmet or shoulder pads, but most were dressed in whatever clothing their mothers were willing to sacrifice on the playing field. In five minutes, the teams were chosen. Peedie was the last chosen, next to Rodney. Peedie ended up on Jack's team. Bill Suggs was captain of the other team.

"Never saw a time before when I'd rather have had a chance to choose Rodney," Jack said to Benjie, who was almost on his side.

"Aw, Peedie's a good kid," said Benjie.

"Yeah," said Jack, "but I'd rather have a good player any day than my little brother."

Right away, things started out bad for Jack's team and Peedie. Jack won the flip and decided to receive first. The kick came to Peedie and he fumbled it – resulting in Billy's team taking their own kickoff for a touchdown.

"Peedie, if you can't catch, just keep away from the ball," growled Jack.

Peedie wiped a tear out of the corner of his eye.

"Aw, forget it, Jack," said Benjie. "It's just a game. Peedie didn't mean to drop the ball."

Jack new that Benjie was right. He was angry mostly because Mother had insisted that Peedie be allowed to play. Also, Jack was feeling low because the other team had scored a touchdown on their own kick off, and were having a big laugh over it.

Again, Billy's team kicked off to Jack's side. Jack's team tried to make some yardage, but was forced to punt on their fourth down.

Billy, playing way back, caught the punt and ran it back to about Jack's 35-yard line. Billy had his cousin, Tubby, on his team. Tubby Suggs was about four feet tall and weighed about 180 lbs. He couldn't move fast, but on the line, he was as solid as the Rock of Gibraltar. He could take out as many tacklers as he was wide.

"Artie, you rush the center this time," said Jack. Artie was on Jack's team and Tubby was Billy's center.

"Me? Rush Tubby? What do you think I are? I couldn't get past that whale if I throwed a harpoon first."

"Come on, Artie, we gotta hold that line."

"Okay, but if Tubby lands on me, I are a dead goose."

"23–36 –79 – *hike!*" said Tubby.

Artie charged three feet, and bounced back six. Billy picked up another twenty yards, before he was brought down by Benjie on about the fifteen-yard line. Rodney was jumping for joy to be on the winning side, for once. He hadn't got his new official Junior League uniform soiled a bit, either.

# Holidays and Hoopla

Throughout the game, Jack's team trailed in points. The teams were fairly even except the scales tipped in Billy's favor – chubby Tubby over teeny Peedie! It was goal-to-go for Jack's team on Billy's one yard line when Jack decided on a most daring plan. It proved to be the high point of the entire game – and also the end of it.

Jack's team was in a huddle. He looked at Billy's line, solid as the wall of China, with Tubby as its keystone. It was then that he struck upon his masterful plan which was, at the time, just a shot in the dark.

"Look," said Jack. "Peedie isn't big enough to run interference, so that leaves us short one blocker. So, this play, we'll try an end run. We're going to let Peedie carry the ball, and we'll run interference for him. I'll take the hike and hand off to Peedie. Peedie, you run for Rodney's end of the line. Get the idea? Whatever you do, keep running and don't lose the ball."

"Oh-kay," said Peedie gulping. "But who's blocking Tubby?" Peedie wasn't sure he could do what he was being asked to do, but he was sport enough to try.

"Don't worry about Tubby. Artie will block him. Won't you, Artie?"

"Sure, I are."

"Okay, let's go," said Jack. "36–26–35– *hike!*"

The ball snapped back. Jack handed it off to Peedie. Peedie ran towards Rodney's end of the line. All that stood between Peedie and the touchdown was Rodney, standing in his impeccably clean white official junior professional National Football League uniform. Peedie was at the line. Rodney had hold of him. Then came a surge of flying, flailing, pushing, piling bodies as probably was never seen before or since. Every player of both teams was in the huge goose-pile. Tubby, who ran the slowest, was last of all. He came barreling in like a runaway steam roller. He landed with a plop that was followed by a big blam. The noise sounded like a pistol shot, ending the game. When the dust settled, the players began climbing out of the pile, one by one. No one on the outside of the pile could tell whether Peedie still had hold of the ball. The boys peeled off the pile like skins off an onion, and formed a circle to see what the outcome would be. A touchdown would put Jack's team ahead for the first time. If the ball wasn't over the line, it would be Billy's first down on his own one yard line. It was *that* close.

"Hurry up," Artie said. "I are squeezed! And I think somebody shooted me, 'cause I heard the bullet."

"Hey, yeah, what was that bang?" said Tubby.

Finally, they got down to Rodney, whose impeccably clean uniform was now dirt smudged. Under Rodney, was Peedie.

Peedie was stretched out flat on the ground. The boys stood around him in a circle. Peedie's eyes were shut tight.

"Peedie," said Jack. "Are you all right?"

Peedie opened his eyes and looked warily up at them. "Can I let go of the ball now?" he asked.

When Peedie got up, all the boys looked down in amazement at the ball. It was flatter than a pizza pie, having burst from all the weight.

Then Jack waved his arms and let out a shout of joy. "Yahoo! It's over the line. It's a touchdown!" Then all of Jack's team cheered wildly and raised Peedie on their shoulders. Peedie had become the hero for the day.

CHAPTER XII

# Memorable Moments in Music

It was a Friday afternoon in December – and Friday the thirteenth, at that. Mrs. Holiday drove Jack uptown to buy a black bow-tie to wear in the school's musical program. The fact that it was Friday the thirteenth didn't worry Jack. He was not particularly superstitious. And, besides, he probably didn't know what the date was, anyway. He never paid much attention to what a calendar said, except around holiday times.

The story would be different for Rodney and Billy Suggs. Because of the musical program, and some unfortunate events, they would be convinced that Friday the thirteenth really meant bad luck. When Jack got home, he tried on his bow tie. For several minutes, he stood before the mirror, craning his neck, struggling to give the tie the right twist. His little brother, Peedie, was watching him.

"How come I didn't get a tie, too, Jack?"

"You're not old enough, Peedie. Anyway, I'm going to be in the all-school musical tonight and you're not."

"What's that?" said Peedie, with his nose pulled up in a wrinkle.

Jack was fighting to straighten his bow tie with his fingertips against the pull of gravity, which kept twisting the tie down like an airplane propeller. "Peedie, why do you always ask so many questions?"

Peedie thought hard. "I don't know, Jack. Why do I?"

Jack went downstairs. "Mom, I can't get this darn tie on right," he complained.

"It isn't necessary for you to get dressed yet, Jack," said Mrs. Holiday. "Wait till after supper. Then we won't take any chances that you'll spill something on your clean white shirt. We're having spaghetti tonight. Put on some old clothes and you and Peedie go out and play for a while."

Outside, Jack and Peedie walked along with their hands in their pockets. The sky overhead was a dull slate color except for a stripe of pink shining through the bare, bristly trees. There were patches of snow on the soaked and flattened grass. Lawns that before invited their running feet would now only get them muddy.

Benjie wasn't home, so Jack and Peedie decided to go to see Rodney. They hoped nothing would be said about the busted football. Invited in by Mr. Van Skotus, they found Rodney practicing his trombone.

"I'm sorry that I can't take time to play with you," said Rodney. "I have a very important solo to play in tonight's concert."

75

"What's that you're putting on your trombone with that nose dropper kind of thing, Rodney?" asked Peedie.

"This? It's my slide oil. You see, I put several drops of it on my trombone slide and it makes it work more smoothly. All great musicians use it." Rodney worked the slide back and forth several times to show Peedie how easily it worked.

"How'd you get picked for the solo?" asked Jack.

"Is there any doubt who's the best trombonist in the school? Of course, Billy Suggs wanted the part. But I play so much better than Billy does that Mr. Farnsworth chose me. Mother says I have my family's natural musical talent."

"Oh?" said Jack. "I didn't know your parents played any instruments."

"They don't. But we have a magnificent stereo system. Haven't you ever noticed our record collection? Now, would you like to hear me perform my solo?" Without waiting for an answer, Rodney began playing. Before he was halfway through, he stopped. He had a pained look on his face and called out: "Mother!"

"Yes, dear, what is it? Did you pinch your little finger in the slide again?"

"No. I've got a sore here." Rodney tugged out his lower lip to show it to her.

"Oh dear, it looks like you've developed a canker sore."

Rodney had lost his confident smile, and his brow was furrowed like a wildly plowed field. "It hurts when I play, Mother. Do something for it."

"My poor darling. I'll call your music director, Mr. Farnsworth. I'm sure he'll know what to do, especially since you have to play such an important trombone solo tonight." Mrs. Van Skotus hurried to the phone, looked in the directory, and dialed Mr. Farnsworth's number.

"Hel-loo, Mr. Farnsworth? This is Elaine Van Skotus, Rodney's mother. Rodney has developed a canker sore on his lip. Yes, his lower lip. And I simply don't know what to do. He says it hurts when he plays his trombone. Of course, you understand the importance of that."

Jack and Peedie could hear Mrs. Van Skotus talking, along with a few intervals of silence when Mr. Farnsworth had a chance to speak.

"But what would you recommend that I do for him?" asked Mrs. Van Skotus. "Alum? No, we don't have any in the medicine chest, but we could stop at the drugstore and get some. You think that might do it? I see. You say it dries up anything? Well, thank you very much, Mr. Farnsworth. As I always say, if you can't trust the specialist, who can you trust? We'll stop at the drugstore and get some alum. Thank you again."

It was seven o'clock in the evening when Mr. Holiday gave Nancy and Jack a ride to school. The school building was lit up like the electric company. The boys and girls in the program had to meet in their classrooms before the program. Mr. & Mrs. Holiday and Peedie went to the auditorium and found seats.

Jack joined the other starched and bow-tied boys in his classroom. He noticed that Ms. Rivera had on bright lipstick and extra curls in her hair. He never remembered seeing her look that fancy before. Everyone seemed to be nervous with before-the-curtain 'butterflies.' The boys paced around the room stiffly with plastered-down hair, while the girls, all in pleats and ruffles, gathered in little groups and smiled like kewpie dolls. Jack saw Jennifer. And to him, she looked the prettiest of all. With Christmas coming, Jack wondered if he dared give her a present. He'd never given a gift to a girl before, except when he'd been forced to go to some silly girl's birthday party. He would want to choose something really nice for Jennifer. The problem was: what could he afford on his small allowance. Just then, Jack saw Rodney.

"Hi, Rodney. How's your lip?"

"It's still sore. Mr. Farnsworth suggested that we get some alum for it, so Mother stopped at the drugstore and bought some. I'm going to ask Miss Jones if I can go down to find out how to use it.

"Attention!' said Ms. Rivera. "All of you who play in the band, please take your instruments down to the band room now."

Betty, Susan, Fred, and Rodney left the room. When they got to the band room, Mr. Farnsworth was ready to direct the "B" band, which was made up of the beginning instrumental students. He looked thinner than ever. He complained that during every concert season, he lost twenty pounds – as if a skeleton-like Mr. Farnsworth could lose any weight and not disappear altogether. There was hardly enough of him to support the growth of his flaming red hair.

"Mr. Farnsworth?"

"Yes, Rodney. Make it quick. I'm all set to go on."

"Mother bought the alum, but my canker sore still hurts my mouth," said Rodney, making a wincing expression.

"Didn't the alum do any good?" asked Mr. Farnsworth, trying to feel casual while looking nervously toward the stage.

"I don't know."

"What do you mean you don't know?" asked Mr. Farnsworth.

"I didn't use any yet. Mother told me to ask you how to use it."

"Oh, for heaven's sakes, Rodney." said Mr. Farnsworth, smoothing back some of his long red hair. "There goes my cue to go on stage. The alum in the jar's not going to do your sore any good unless you put some of it in your mouth." With that, Mr. Farnsworth leaped on stage like a gazelle.

Meanwhile, the rest of the class who sang in the chorus formed in a line and marched down to stand in the wings of the auditorium to wait their turn to perform.

Jack was surprised to see Billy Suggs in the same line with him. Teachers, helping in the program, were shushing everyone, so Jack had to whisper.

"Sst, Billy!"

"Oh, hi, Jack," Billy whispered back.

"I thought you were going to play in the band," said Jack.

"Aw, there's only one trombone part. And after we practiced it, Mr. Farnsworth gave it to Rodney."

"How come?"

"I think it's because Rodney's trombone is newer and shines better than mine and doesn't have any dents in it. I can play as good as Rodney anytime. Probably even better. Besides, Rodney's an apple polisher." After Billy told Jack this, his expression suddenly brightened and he caught a little snicker behind his hand, like he had a private joke.

"You don't seem too unhappy about it all," said Jack.

Billy snickered to himself again.

"Hey, what's the joke," said Jack, looking down. "Is my bow tie on crooked or something?"

Billy shook his head but still kept grinning like something was going to happen that he could hardly wait for.

"Come on, Billy, be a buddy and let me in on it," pleaded Jack.

"Well," said Billy, looking all around to make sure that no one was listening in. "You promise not to tell on me?"

Jack was so eager to find out what was amusing Billy, that he was ready to promise anything.

"Cross your heart," said Billy. "And no crossing your fingers, toes, or anything like that."

Jack took the oath like a supreme court justice.

"Okay. You remember when Rodney was talking at the front of the room with Ms. Rivera?" Billy cupped his hand and whispered into Jack's ear. "That's when I opened his trombone case and filled his slide oil bottle with glue."

Jack caught his breath as his mouth gaped open at the thought of it. Glue in Rodney's slide oil bottle! Jack grit his teeth, as the thought of what would happen to Rodney's trombone with glue in the slide instead of oil went through his mind.

It was just minutes before Jack's class was to do their part of the program when Jack saw Rodney come up to Mr. Farnsworth. Rodney had a very weird look on his face, stranger than usual. It looked like he'd chewed a whole lemon. Instead of speaking to Mr. Farnsworth, he was tugging on his arm.

"What is it, Rodney?" bellowed Mr. Farnsworth, still keyed-up with program jitters.

78

Rodney was excitedly pointing to his mouth which was pursed like a small volcano.

"Speak up, Rodney. Say something."

"Wook, wook, wook!" said Rodney

"Oh, for heavens sakes, Rodney! What did you do?" Mr. Farnsworth clapped his hand on his red head. "How much alum did you use?" Rodney showed him the half-empty jar. "You won't be able to un-pucker for a week! Why do these things always have to happen to me – and just at concert time? What am I going to do about your part? You're sure not going to be able to play the trombone with *that* prickled-up puss."

While Mr. Farnsworth was deciding that it was time for him to jump off a balcony, Rodney got an idea.

"Miher Warnwhir. Miher Warnwhir." Rodney pointed over to his class, as they were climbing onto the risers ready to sing their part of the program. Rodney tried to make himself understood. "Beewee Uggs! Beewee Uggs!"

"What are you trying to say?" said Mr. Farnsworth. "Pee Wee Uggs? Oh, Wait. I get you. Billy Suggs. Sure, Billy knows your part."

It didn't take long for Mr. Farnsworth to hustle Billy out of line and push the music into his hands. "Billy, you've got to do Rodney's solo. He's not going to be able to do it. Hurry, get out on stage. I'll announce it."

"But,… but," said Billy, nearly swept off his feet.

"No buts about it, Billy. You're the only one besides Rodney who knows this part."

"But Mr. Farnsworth, I left my trombone at home."

With that, Mr. Farnsworth grabbed Rodney's trombone from him and thrust it into Billy's hands. "Then you'll have to borrow Rodney's."

Before Billy knew quite what was happening to him, he was standing in the center of the stage in front of a music stand and hearing Mr. Farnsworth announce to the audience that he, Billy, was taking Rodney's place.

Billy hastily arranged the music on the stand and took up Rodney's trombone. Then Mr. Farnsworth raised his baton and the band began to play.

What happened then is history, and made Friday the thirteenth take on real meaning for Billy. By the time the band was well into the number, Billy discovered that the slide on Rodney's trombone was beginning to get sticky. It began to pull like taffy. He pushed easy slide positions past their mark, flatting the note. Then when he tried to pull the slide back, it dragged so much, the trombone mouth-piece nearly mashed his teeth.

Billy's sour notes caused the perspiration to pour down Mr. Farnsworth's face. And Billy turned all colors of the rainbow. He had one more solo section to go. By that time, Billy's knuckles were white from gripping the horn and the slide in his clenched fists. Instead of a musician, he looked like an athlete trying to develop muscles with a gym exerciser. Finally, although he was tugging with all his might, he couldn't budge the slide at all. The melody that was supposed to go – Ba-da-ba-da-dup-a-do-ba, came out like a "Johnny-one-note" – blah, blah, blah!

After the concert was over, almost everyone in the audience thought Billy's strange performance had been a case of the jitters or stage-fright. Only Jack, besides Billy himself, knew what really had happened – that Billy had 'got stuck' in his own joke.

CHAPTER XIII

# Sniffles and Saturdays

It was the second week after the all-school musical program. A huge snowstorm blanketed the Midwest. A cold front swept over the Great Lakes region. And the temperature dipped. Jack was in school waiting for lunch time.

The school heating system was the kind that alternately froze and toasted a person, or sometimes both at the same time. Following such ups and downs in temperature, there were always ups and downs in sickness, too. On this Thursday, there were several empty desks. Most of the absences were blamed on the flu. But the line between health and sickness was never clear cut, for each room had its share of snifflers and hackers and nose dribblers. On this Thursday, Arthur was one of them.

"Ah – a-a- choo!" sneezed Artie.

"Here's your composition," said Jack, picking up the paper that had blown off Artie's desk. It was Artie's English paper, to anyone able to read his handwriting.

"Dhanks. I are got da snivvles."

"You're telling me: I wish you'd aim in another direction or hand out some towels." Jack held his breath while the sneeze cloud settled.

"I dried to catch dat one, bud id gott away. Did I sprayed you?" Artie wiped his nose with a shredded Kleenex.

"Did you? Just look at your English paper. It looks like it was rained on or something."

"Artie looked down at the sprinkled and smeary paper. "I guess my Kleenex wored out."

"Why don't you ask Ms. Rivera for another one?"

"She always bawls me oud if I ask for more'n one a week."

"Jack and Arthur. Stop your talking," said Ms. Rivera, looking their way. The room settled back to the silence of the ticking clock. The clock's ticking was not a bad sound, since it ticked off school time passing. Only to Jack, it ticked too slowly to be much comfort. Finally, it ticked up to lunch time.

Since the night of the musical program, nobody spoke above a whisper about Billy Sugg's botched trombone solo. While he struggled through that performance, everyone had cringed and tugged and suffered with him. And other than Billy, only Jack knew why the solo had gone so sour. But Billy often pulled pranks – and Rodney was often the butt of them. Something about Rodney just seemed to ask for it. This had been one prank, however, that frankly had backfired and justice had won out. And Jack was still wondering what happened to Rodney's trombone after that.

81

He was dying to ask, but he didn't dare to. He was sure that if he *did* ask, he'd get blamed for putting glue in the horn.

In the cafeteria, Fred was next in line to Jack.

"Hi, Jack," said Fred, as he set his tray down on the table and sat down himself. "Did you hear about Rodney's trombone?"

Jack shook his head. When he wanted to play dumb, he could put on an angel act till you could almost see wings sprouting.

"Well, let me tell you what Rodney told me. Remember the trouble that Billy had playing the solo in the concert? It was because somebody put glue in Rodney's trombone slide."

"Do they know who did it?" asked Jack.

"No."

Jack drank some of his milk. He almost wished they *did* know who had done it, for Jack was beginning to feel guilty himself, just knowing that Billy was to blame. "What happened to the horn? Was it ruined?"

"Almost. Rodney told me his dad had a terrible time with it. The slide was glued on tight."

"Was Rodney's dad able to fix it?"

"Yes, but only after he boiled the horn in hot water. But that wasn't the end of it."

"It wasn't?"

"No. After Mr. Van Skotus had boiled the horn and got the slide off and cleaned it, it got glued again."

"Glued again!" repeated Jack, nearly dropping his milk into his baked beans. "How come?'

"It seems that after Mr. Van Skotus had got the trombone all cleaned, Rodney went to oil it and well, you won't believe this – there was glue in the slide oil bottle. So, the slide was glued again and had to be cleaned again."

"Did Rodney tell you, I mean, let on to you who he thought did it?"

"Naw. They blamed it on bad luck, since the concert was held on Friday the thirteenth, and all. They're making up a list of things that are bad luck now."

"Who is?"

"Billy and Rodney. Come on, let's take our trays back."

As they lined up to return their trays, Jack couldn't help wondering about what Fred had told him. Billy had played a trick on Rodney, and also ended up getting fooled himself. And now, both Billy and Rodney were blaming it on Friday the thirteenth. Jack couldn't help thinking that this was certainly a screwy business.

Back in the room, the tattle-tale clock said "Back to school-work." Everyone was really knuckling down because another report card was coming up, and they knew it was their last chance to up their grades. Every year it was the same thing. The teachers, and sometimes the principal, would encourage each child to work harder. Some kids followed that advice. Some would work the same. And some, maybe not as much. The kids that were good in school would get A's and B's and not seem to work too hard. The kids that typically struggled would seem to do the same amount of work, yet end up with lower marks. Each year seemed more or less like the last. Nobody changed their report card grades much. Just like the time Donald had broken his leg and missed half a year of school. When he came back, he was no dumber than before.

Ms. Rivera, at her desk at the front of the room, looked down in her plan book. The class was all seated and waiting for the teacher's announcement.

"Let me see," said Ms. Rivera, running her finger down the list of topics she'd assigned. "Today it's your turn to give your history report, Mary Jane. Are you ready?"

Mary Jane had a big TV-toothpaste smile, like not even an earthquake could stop her from giving her report.

"All right, Mary Jane. Bring your report to the front of the room, please."

Jack was all set to slouch down in his chair. The chair was hard as a rock, and his torso had to squirm in places to get comfortable, but Jack didn't mind listening. He was a pretty good listener. Sometimes he even remembered what was said. Here he was just getting nicely settled when Ms. Rivera spoke to him:

"Jack, don't forget about tomorrow. It's your turn to give your report on the rise and fall of the Roman empire."

*Ulp!* That made Jack sit up. He'd forgotten all about that. It'd been days ago when he'd got the assignment, and he'd put it out of his mind from that day on. Jack didn't know whether Rome had cracked open like San Francisco, or sunk in the ocean like Atlantis. And he was going to have to follow Mary Jane, the biggest brain in the class. Jack didn't hear a word of Mary Jane's report – at least not a word *stuck*. All he could do was sit bolt upright and stew in his own juice. If he could have followed someone like Artie, he might have stood a chance. But now he felt already shot down.

The rest of the day was a complete blank to Jack. If he'd had his wits about him, he probably could have copied something out of an encyclopedia. But to follow Mary Jane, he knew he didn't stand a ghost of a chance. It puzzled Jack how some girls could sit still in one place for so long and patch together such a big report and then, like Mary Jane, get all giddy about it, to boot. Jack was feeling so desperate, he was just about reduced to asking her for help. He knew he'd have to swallow a lot of pride. He also knew her price for help would be ever-lasting enslavement, enough to fill two prisons.

# Holidays and Hoopla

For a while when he got home, Jack scratched around through some books to see what he could dig up on the subject. When Jack read that there was more than one Roman Empire, he felt paralyzed. He didn't know whether to report on the Holy one or the other one. It was then that his very active mind went into high gear, and his body helped.

First his nose sniffled, just slightly. Then he wiggled it. Then he swallowed and tested his throat. Then he put his hand on the back of his neck and stretched. Then he felt his forehead. Next, he was at the mirror with his tongue hanging out. "Ah-h-h." Then he tested out his frown. He had a little cold all right, but it was beginning to grow to epidemic size.

With the symptoms, came a reason for them – Artie, of course. He'd had a cold and had kept sneezing at Jack. Jack felt that he was contagious already. Preventative medicine was in order, which, at the least, would require quarantine.

When Jack had his symptoms sufficiently worked up, he went to see his mother. She was getting out the supper dishes.

"Mom, I feel awful."

"That's too bad, Jack. Where do you hurt?" said Mrs. Holiday with genuine concern.

"Kind of all over. I think I'm coming down with a cold or something bigger."

"Why do you think that, Jack?"

"Well, I sit by Artie and he kept sneezing and looked kind of bubonic."

"Maybe you better go up and get in bed," suggested Mrs. Holiday.

Getting in bed before supper and before his favorite TV shows and before bedtime, too, were symptoms Mrs. Holiday didn't dare overlook. That night, Mrs. Holiday gave Jack some cold pills and drubbed on some strong-smelling grease whose fumes could penetrate three layers of blankets, and gave the bedroom the appropriate sickroom smell.

The next morning, Mrs. Holiday came in and woke Jack to see if he'd improved. He did indeed have a cold. The question was how severe it was. And was it bad enough to keep Jack home from school? Jack's final test would be by the ordeal of cold medicine.

Most times when it came to choosing between this form of medieval torture and school, school won out. But this Friday it was medieval-torture medicine versus school *and* a history report. And Jack was determined to suffer through the lesser evil. For Jack, choosing was often a choice between two rather unappetizing situations. One hinged on the other. It was either chores or no play, spinach or no dessert, school or sick-in-bed.

"Jack," said Mrs. Holiday. "I think we'd better do something for your throat. It's for your own good."

Whenever anything was for his own good, Jack knew it had to be pretty awful. And Jack had, indeed, guessed right and dreaded its coming. But there was no getting away from it; no avoiding it. It was fate. It was destiny. It was mouthwash.

Jack followed his mother to the bathroom to gargle.

Mrs. Holiday poured a generous portion of the vinegary stuff into a glass, and then handed it to Jack. He stood before the bathroom sink and slowly twirled the golden liquid around and around. It was the stuff they advertised on TV that made all kinds of silly dames want to kiss you – and was poison to germs, besides.

Jack held his breath and took a big slug of it. The stuff was as tasty as kerosene and as strong as turpentine. While Jack was in the middle of a gargle, Peedie came in full of his usual questions. Jack nearly gagged.

"How come you're not dressed for school yet, Jack? You're going to be late."

"Jack isn't going to school today. He's got a cold," said Mrs. Holiday. Peedie got a real suspicious look on his face. He went off to school testing himself to see if *he* had a cold.

In no time at all, the school day passed and Peedie and Nancy were home. They came in and went out to play again with their friends, when something suddenly dawned on Jack.

"Holy cow!" Jack thought to himself. "I've faked myself out again." Jack, like any other boy in his right mind, would never get sick on the day before the weekend. And tomorrow was *Saturday*! To Jack that was a disaster, for it meant he'd probably end up stuck in bed on a day when he didn't even have to go to school.

CHAPTER XIV

# A Visit from St. Nick

On the third week in December, vacation arrived. No more being dragged from under warm covers by the jarring of an alarm clock buzzer. No more being hustled off to school. No more worrying about school reports due. The Christmas vacation meant that Jack would have to plan his own life, except what the holiday demanded of him.

Now was the night before Christmas and all through the Holiday house everyone was stirring, even Butterball, the Holiday's pet cat. He seemed to sense the excitement of the holiday as much as anyone. Maybe it was the way Peedie went leaping around the house and rolling over the footstool. Or maybe it was Jack's big smile. Or maybe it was the way Nancy petted Butterball. Whatever it was, Butterball's big yellow eyes seemed to glow more than usual. He no longer batted the Christmas tree ornaments with his paw like he did as a kitten, but he studied the brightly decorated tree, his tail gently swaying, as if perhaps remembering other Christmases.

Jack had finally picked out a gift for Jennifer. After much thought, he had decided on flowers. It was less embarrassing than shopping at stores with ladies' things. He had thought to buy Jennifer a bouquet, but his budget forced him to settle for a single flower – a pink carnation. Mr. Schrader, the florist, placed it in white tissue paper and put it in a box wrapped with a pink ribbon. Mr. Schrader even gave him a card to sign his name. It was a glorious sight to behold.

Jack delivered the package himself. He put it on her porch, rang the bell, and ran off. The thought of her opening the box was thrilling to him – and a little scary, too.

At home, Jack never mentioned that he'd bought a present, so he had to hide his excitement. Little Peedie was so excited looking forward to Christmas Day that he could hardly wait. Around Peedie, Jack acted calmer because he felt more grown up.

"Peedie," said Jack, with a hint of mischief in his voice. "I'll bet there's one thing you forgot to ask Santa Clause for on your list."

Peedie smiled and tried to guess.

"Was it something we saw on TV?"

"Like what?"

"Like a Creepy Monster Kit?"

"No, but it's something you should have put on the top of your list. It's something you need very much." Jack was leading Peedie on. Peedie loved riddles, but only when given the answer.

Peedie puzzled to himself. "What didn't I write down that I should have?"

87

"Do you give up?" asked Jack.

Peedie knew he was being put on, but he hoped to think of a snappy comeback. "Okay, I'll bite, what is it?"

"It's funny you should say that, Peedie," giggled Jack. "Because you should have asked Santa for your two front teeth."

Peedie's answer to that was a pillow thrown at Jack that nearly hit the Christmas tree. He wasn't really sore, but he didn't like being teased about his missing baby teeth. Mr. Holiday looked up from his newspaper.

"Hey, Peedie, be careful. Do you want to knock over our tree before Santa gets here?"

"Jack was teasing me."

"Jack, you'd better find something else to do."

"Could we open some of the presents that came through the mail?"

Not until tomorrow. But I notice one thing you should do that you haven't done yet."

"What's that, Dad?"

"You haven't hung up your stockings by the fire, and it's almost bedtime."

"Oh, yeah. Where are they?"

"I don't know. You'll have to ask Mother or Nancy to help you find them."

"Dad," said Peedie. "Do you think Aunt Lulu would lend me one of her stockings?"

"Why, Peedie? Don't you think Jack will be able to find yours?"

"It's not that. It's just that – well – hers would be much bigger than the one I've got."

"Oh, Silly, go with Jack and help him find them, or it'll be too late to hang them up." Mr. Holiday couldn't help chuckling over Peedie's funny ideas.

Soon, the stockings had been properly hung. One for Jack, one for Nancy, and one for Peedie. Nancy stood admiring the brilliant Christmas tree with its shiny tinsel and ornaments. She, more than anyone else in the family, loved pretty things. She had also decorated her own room.

"It's time that you were all bundled into your beds,' said Mrs. Holiday.

"Will you leave something out for Santa's reindeers, Mom?" said Peedie.

"Yes, I won't forget his reindeer," said Mrs. Holiday.

Nancy petted Butterball one last time before she started up the stairs. Then the cat curled up to go to sleep. Nancy could hardly wait for morning when she would give Butterball his Christmas present, a catnip mouse.

Mother and Father tucked the children in bed and kissed each one before shutting off the lights. Then Mr. & Mrs. Holiday went downstairs. At the bottom of the stairs, Mr. Holiday turned and said:

"Dorothy, what do you want to bet that Peedie will be the first one up tomorrow morning?"

"I wouldn't want to bet much," said Mrs. Holiday, "because I think you're probably right. Jack and Nancy act so grown-up, and they're not as excitable as they used to be.

"All right. I'll give you odds. A dollar to a donut says Peedie will be the first one up.

"I'll risk a donut," said Mrs. Holiday.

Upstairs, all was quiet and dark. The cool covers were beginning to warm to the children snuggled under them.

"Psst, Jack, are you awake?"

"Uh, what?"

"I said, are you awake?" whispered Peedie.

"I am now, thanks to you," said Jack. "What do you want, Peedie? I was just falling asleep. How come you're not asleep yet?"

"Because I just got an idea. You know what I'm going to do?"

Jack yawned. "Peedie, tell me about it in the morning. I want to get to sleep."

Peedie was silent. The room was dark, except for a sprinkling of moonlight. It was so quiet, Jack could almost hear Peedie thinking in the dark.

"Okay, Peedie. I know that you'll never be able to get to sleep unless you can tell me what your idea is. So go ahead and tell me."

Peedie bounced out of bed and sat on the edge of Jack's bed.

"Jack, you know what I'm going to do? I'm going to stay awake so I can see Santa Claus!"

"Oh, Peedie, is that what you woke me up for? You can stay awake if you want to. I'm tired and I want to get some sleep so I'll be rested for tomorrow. Goodnight." Jack rolled over, hoping Peedie would go to sleep.

Peedie tiptoed back across the room. The floor was cool to his bare feet. With his eyes open wide, things looked only gray in shadow and silhouette. Peedie listened for house noises, but all was quiet. He crept over to peek out the window before getting back into bed. Outside, the snow shimmered in the moonlight like it was freckled with glitter paint. For some minutes, his eyes scanned the deep purple sky. Then, feeling a little chilly, Peedie got back in his bed. *I might as well be comfortable while I wait*, he thought. *It may be quite a while till Santa gets here.*

Peedie lay back on his bed smiling to himself. A shiver of ticklishness went through him. He decided he'd better put his feet under the covers. They'd gotten cold while he stood at the window. *Gosh, it gets boring waiting. I hope he doesn't take too much longer to get here*, thought Peedie.

*I guess I'll just close my eyes and listen for him for a while. I'm tired of staring out the window.*

It was so quiet, Peedie could hear Jack breathing. *I wonder what I'll hear first*, he thought. *Will I hear sleigh bells, or maybe the clomping of reindeer hooves, or maybe a neigh from one of his reindeer? Come to think of it, do reindeer neigh or whinny? Gee, it's hard waiting and waiting.*

Then a mist passed before his eyes and the sky seemed to glow and sparkle with stars. And Peedie heard a sort of slicing sound. He smiled to himself like a scientist making a discovery. *Why didn't I think of that? Santa's reindeer would be too well trained to make any noise. Reindeer are very quick and light footed, but the runners of a sleigh loaded with toys would be bound to make some noise in landing. That must be Santa Claus landing on the roof. I'll sneak downstairs and see.*

Peedie crept down the stairs ever so quietly and hid by the fireplace to watch. At first, he saw nothing except Butterball curled up under the tree sound asleep. He listened with all his might. Then he heard a bump and a thump. Was it the fat old fellow himself dropping down the chimney? At that moment, it suddenly dawned on Peedie. What if Santa should find him there hiding by the fireplace, then what? He peeked out to see. Sure enough, he had not hidden himself well enough. A big round fellow in a big red suit was standing looking right at him. Peedie had seen Santa's helpers in stores before. Some that put on fake beards. But this Santa was just like Peedie had always imagined he would be. He was big and roly-poly with a fur collar and cuffs on his red suit, and a dangly white, tasseled hat. And he had the rosiest cheeks and eyes that twinkled like starlight.

*Could this all be happening to me*? thought Peedie, who now worried that perhaps Santa would be angry with him for sneaking down and peaking. If Santa Clause were angry, then what? Santa sat himself down in Dad's chair. And to Peedie's surprise, he smiled at him and beckoned him to come over and see him. Peedie approached him cautiously. But as he stood at the jovial fellow's knee, Santa hoisted him onto his lap.

"Your name must be Phillip Douglas Holiday," said Santa.

"They call me Peedie," said Peedie.

All right then, Peedie it is. You know it is very, very late for you to be up."
Peedie nodded. "And you must also know that I have much to do, especially on this night of all nights. So, why aren't you in your bed?"

Peedie thought and thought, but couldn't answer.
"Don't be afraid. You're *not* afraid of me, are you?"

Peedie nodded "yes," then he nodded "no", then he nodded something in between.

90

"Maybe," said Santa, "you had a question you wished to ask me, is that it?"

Peedie nodded definitely "yes".

"All right, but you must ask me quickly and it must be short because I have many calls to make."

"Ah, Santa, is – is your beard real?"

"Is my beard real? Ho, ho, ho," laughed Santa. "Why don't you just give it a little tug and see."

So Peedie gave Santa's beard a tug, ever so gently, and found that it was as real as could be.

Santa was so amused by Peedie's question, that he laughed and laughed till he shook and he jiggled. He jiggled and wiggled till Peedie felt he would never stop.

"Santa, if you don't stop jiggling, I think I will fall right off your knee."

"What, Peedie? What? For gosh sakes, what are you mumbling about, Peedie?"

Peedie rubbed his hand over his eyes and looked up to see Jack bending over him shaking him.

"Come on, Peedie. Wake up. Wake up!"

Peedie sat up in bed. "Huh?"

It's Christmas morning, dopey. Everybody else is up and ready to go downstairs and open their presents. I thought I was never going to be able to get you to wake up.

So Peedie was the last one up, after all. Mrs. Holiday had won her dollar. For that one time, Mr. Holiday lost his bet. Peedie never *did* tell the family how he had seen Santa Claus that Christmas night.

CHAPTER XV

# Inventions, Disasters, and Discoveries

The excitement started early Christmas morning when Peedie, Nancy, and Jack dashed down the stairs like an avalanche crashing down a mountain. The mysterious packages under the Christmas tree were beautiful to see – all stickered and ribboned and gaily wrapped. In seconds, the wrappings were torn to shreds and the children jumped like lightning from toy to game and game to toy. They were all "oohs' and "ahs' and big wide grins. The rumpus was such that their cat stood at the door wanting to get out. But Nancy suddenly remembered his Christmas present, a catnip mouse, and gave it to him. Then Butterball, too, joined in the festivities.

For that day, nothing less than a stick of dynamite could have kept the Holiday children from enjoying their toys. Every gift, every game piece was spread out before their adoring eyes. Nancy had dressed her new doll with its entire wardrobe. Peedie had test-driven every new toy car and truck. Jack had investigated every partition of every game and tried each moving part. Mr. and Mrs. Holiday joined in the excitement like children themselves. Mother showed Nancy ways of caring for her new doll, and Father ran Peedie's racing car, hardly giving Peedie a turn.

Finally, a couple of days passed, and with it passed the piled-up giddiness of the holiday. And then some arguments began. Jack complained that Peedie didn't play his secret agent game right. And Peedie complained that Jack hogged his cars. And Nancy complained that Peedie had shot her doll with his cork gun. Mrs. Holiday, whose nerves sometimes became ragged from such squabbles, suggested that they all play outside for a while, or go see what their friends were doing.

It was just then that Jack was invited to play at Rodney's house. Rodney, being an only child, escaped the problem of squabbling brothers and sisters and so was always happy to have company, especially during Christmas time when he had so many super toys to show off.

Jack clomped trough the gray slushy snow with his boots. It was mild out and rivulets of water ran along the curb from the melting snow. He thought about the pink carnation, though he hadn't heard a word from Jennifer. He wondered how he should act when he saw her again. Then Jack noticed several cars parked in the street near Rodney's house. Rodney came to the door after Jack rang the back doorbell.

"Come in, Jack. We were just playing with my road race set," said Rodney with a big smile.

Jack took off his coat and boots and followed Rodney in, wondering who Rodney meant by "we". As he entered the kitchen, Jack noticed that Rodney's mother was wearing blue eye shadow and dangly gold earrings. On the kitchen counters were buffet platters with stacks of teeny-weeny sandwiches and other dainty and decorative treats.

"Be sure you keep the boys in the playroom, dear, and remember the other things I told you about."

"Yes, Mother," answered Rodney.

In the hallway before the door of the play room, Jack could hear the whirr and buzz of a racing set.

"What was that all about?" asked Jack.

"What?"

"What your mother was talking about."

"Oh, that. Mother's having Bridge Club today."

The noise of the racing set was louder as they opened the playroom door and went in. Jack looked down and saw a boy in a plaid shirt playing with the racers. It was Artie with his nose almost glued to the track. Artie had the knobs turned all the way up and the cars zoomed like mad.

The racing set was one of those super deluxe models with switches and bridges and loop-the-loops, just like on the front page of the Sears, Roebuck & Company toy catalog. It wasn't until Artie had crashed the cars off the bridge, that he looked up to see Rodney and Jack standing there.

"Boy, you're driving those cars real crazy," said Jack.

"Sure, I are. I didn't saw you came in."

Your problem is you don't run it correctly," said Rodney. "It takes skill. Let me show you how it should be done." Rodney took over. And as he played with the set, he told Artie and Jack how, in the Grand-Prix, the racers only do such and such, and that the cars should never, ever be run at this speed or that speed, and they should only go up and down or around in this or that direction.

Jack yawned, and he and Artie looked at each other. Then, although Rodney blabbed on, the two boys began to look around the room for something else to do.

"Bing, bam, rat-a-tat-tat, blam!" It was Artie. He had found a new drum set and was trying it out. He was so engrossed, he forgot he had a note from Jennifer to give Jack.

"Hey, Artie, don't play that," said Rodney in a hushed voice.

"Why? Are I doing it wrong?"

"Mother is having a Bridge party and she told me we couldn't make any noise."

"What else did you get for Christmas, Rodney?" said Jack as Rodney turned off the racing set and put away the drumsticks.

"Oh, let me show you," he said. Here are my new skis."

"Golly, have you tried them out yet?" asked Jack.

"No, Mother says I must have lessons first. She's afraid I'll sprain something."

94

Artie chuckled. "With your luck, you'd probably sprain your brain."

"What else did you get?" asked Jack.

"I got a foto-electric football game."

"Foto-electric?" said Jack. "What does that mean?"

"You set your team players up and the electric board makes them move till they score a touchdown."

"That sounds great! Let's play!" said Jack.

"Nah, I've been playing with that all morning. Besides, my mom got tired of the buzzing. Let me show you what else I got. Come over here."

Jack and Artie followed Rodney to another corner of the playroom. Rodney opened the cover of a huge toy construction set. The box was filled with girders, and gears, and pulleys, and motors. A full color picture pasted inside the box cover showed a boy smiling fantastically and operating a derrick by remote control, while a man, probably the boy's father, looked on proudly.

Rodney brought out another box. It was a set of soldiers.

"See. I also got these. Notice how they're all hand-painted and authentic in every detail."

Artie's face lit up with an idea. "Let's make us a tower outa the set and we'll have a war with them soldiers and they can get shooted and fall off the top of the tower." Jack liked the idea and was all set to second the suggestion when Rodney vetoed it with a shocked look on his face.

"No, we couldn't do that," Rodney said. "We might scratch one of the soldiers. Besides, my father doesn't want me to build anything with the set, unless he's with me to help with the plans.

Artie looked sympathetically downcast and said: "It are a shame with all the toys you got for Christmas, Rodney, that you didn't get none you could play with."

"Oh, I got plenty of those," said Rodney.

"Like what?" asked Jack.

"Well, for one thing I got a complete chemistry set. Only thing is, it's in the basement."

"What's the matter with it being in the basement?"

"On account of Mother's Bridge party. Mother wants us to play here in the playroom."

"For gosh sakes. The party isn't being held in the basement, is it? We could be real quiet."

"Yes," added Artie, "I are as quiet as a mouse."

"All right, I'll show it to you. But be quiet, though."

Rodney led the way, and Artie and Jack followed him down the cellar stairs. The basement was almost as neat as a living room. Anything that got the least bit faded or worn at Rodney's house was donated to the Salvation Army. Against the wall on a table especially fitted out for it, was a complete chemistry set: shelves and shelves of little boxes of powders and crystals, and liquids in tiny vials. Each container was labeled with names such as: sulfur, magnesium, potassium, sodium, and calcium nitrate. In another compartment was a little rack with test tubes, tweezers, and eyedroppers, bunches of glass tubing, a tiny balancing scale, and an alcohol lamp. Rodney pulled the switch on the fluorescent light over the table and after it blinkered on, the chemistry set looked just as shiny as it has at the store. Jack's and Artie's eyes nearly bugged out. Rodney sat down at the table.

"Watch me," said Rodney, taking a little piece of bluish-purple paper from a tiny box and putting a drop of chemical on it. "There, see that?" said Rodney proudly. "It turned red."

Artie scratched the back of his head. "So. What are that supposed to show?"

"The litmus test indicates the chemical is acid, not alkaline."

"Can't you make anything useful?" asked Jack.

"Like what?"

Well, like invisible ink so we could play spy and send secret messages."

"Certainly. There's a formula for it right in the book that came with the set."

It took a while as Rodney measured out each ingredient precisely and took great pains to stir them as directed in the book. It was tedious watching and waiting, but the wait seemed worth it – to actually make invisible ink!

"There, it's done," said Rodney sitting back proudly.

"Finally," said Jack. Now what are we going to write with?"

"I don't know what you guys think, but are there anything wrong with using a pen?"

"Obviously not. But I don't have a pen down here. And to get one, I'd have to sneak upstairs in the middle of Mother's Bridge party, and I don't know whether I should do that," said Rodney.

"Look," said Jack, taking command of the situation. If you were in a dungeon of an old castle and wanted to keep your real identity a secret, would you send out for a pen so you could write with your invisible ink? Of course not. You'd make do with what you had in your prison cell, wouldn't you?"

Rodney seemed to understand Jack's point, because he snapped his fingers and said:

"How about trying to write with the tweezers in my chemistry set?"

"Okay," said Jack.

The boys bunched their heads together while Rodney dipped the tweezers into the water-like invisible ink, and scratched something over a piece of paper.

"There, it's done," said Rodney.

Artie picked up the scrap of paper and looked at it under the light. First, he twisted his head one way, then another. Then he turned the paper over and over. It was plain to see that he was puzzled.

"What's the matter, Artie?" Rodney asked.

"What good are that ink? I can't see nothing on this paper."

"Of course not. It's invisible ink," answered Jack. "You wouldn't expect a guard to smuggle out a note for a prisoner with writing on it, would you? You get it, don't you, Rodney?"

"Well, sort of Jack, only…"

"Only what?"

"With that invisible ink, I couldn't figure where I'd started writing and where I'd left off."

"That's all right, Rodney," said Jack. "A spy would write in a secret code, anyway."

By this time, Artie had become bored. "I are sick of making ink I can't even see. Can't cha make something useful like a great discovery, or rockets, or bombs, or nothing like that?"

"I don't know how to go about making anything that isn't in the book," said Rodney.

"Aw, that's easy," said Jack. "How is anything great discovered?"

Artie raised an eyebrow.

"I aren't sure."

It's easy. All we gotta do, if we want to invent something, is mix lots of stuff together and hope. Because all great discoveries were accidents. I've seen it lots of times in the movies."

"I guess if it's in the movies, it are true. Anyhow, I are for trying it. Anything will be better'n that invisible ink."

Rodney wasn't as eager to experiment as Jack or Artie, but he went along with it. First, they lit the alcohol lamp, and then they started putting pinches of chemicals in a test tube until they watched the contents bubble up.

"Did you discover anything yet?" asked Rodney, watching the bubbly mixture and biting his fingernails.

"Let's add more of that yellow stuff."

"Sulfur?"

"Yeah, and put some more of this in, too," said Artie. "We should discover something, because I sure are hoping hard enough."

"Man, look at that fizz! Isn't that a gas, though?"

Meanwhile upstairs, the Bridge Club ladies were enjoying their gossip and refreshments. The ladies had played several hands of Bridge and now were getting tea or coffee and helping themselves to dessert. At first, they chattered loudly in little groups, scattered about the living room and dining room. But then, unaccountably, the talking gave way to some rather loud and nervous whispering.

Mrs. Yeager had a sour look on her face as she whispered behind her hand to Mrs. Sagerstown.

"Have you noticed anything about Henrietta lately? I was just chatting with her, but had to get away before I gagged. Her breath was awful. Somebody should hand out some mints or something."

"Let me tell you what happened to *me*," said Mrs. Sagerstown. "I got this big piece of cheesecake. Now, you know how I simply love cheesecake. Well, let me tell you, I went to take a bite of it – and I nearly vomited. I'll bet Henrietta ate some of that awful cheesecake. It smelled rotten."

Then, in the living room, Mrs. Brinkwater was overheard to say, "It's a crime nowadays what some people will pass off as perfume!"

It wasn't long before many of the ladies had handkerchiefs to their noses and were casting suspicious looks at each other, or else were looking for some polite way of leaping out a window.

Then Mrs. Steinmiller said to Rodney's mother, "My dear, do you smell something burning?"

By that time, Mrs. Van Skotus had broken out in a regular rash of perspiration. She ran to the kitchen to check the stove. Then she noticed smoke curling under the door to the cellar. When she opened the door, she was greeted with the full stench of it.

In the meantime, all the ladies left in a hurry – if running outdoor coatless in mid-winter can be called in a hurry. Even Jack and Artie, the great inventors themselves, left before the height of their gassy triumph. They beat it out the back door. They had stuck it out as long as they could bear it. Outside, they slowed down to a walk and caught their breath.

Columbus had discovered America by accident and thought it was the Indies. What the boys had discovered was not as glorious as that, but for all they knew, they had discovered the world's greatest stink bomb!"

When they arrived at Jack's house, Artie suddenly got a concerned look on his face and started poking through all his coat pockets.

"What are you looking for?" asked Jack.

"Oh, good." said Artie, with a sigh of relief. "I are got a note to give you. Jennifer asked me to deliver it."

Artie handed Jack the note and walked off toward home.

Nervously, Jack unfolded the paper and read:

*Dear Jack,*

*I loved my present. It was beautiful and smelled just like spring.*

*Lots of love,*

*Jennifer*

*What a world!* thought Jack, feeling warm inside. His life had all the ups and downs of a go-cart ride – fun and boredom, certainty and doubt, pink carnations and stink bombs. Never in his life had he experienced a big finish like on a TV show. To him, endings were always beginnings.

At least now he could face returning to school after Christmas vacation, for he knew he would be seeing Jennifer once again.

## CHAPTER XVI

# Jack Slips Again

The New Year came and ended the vacation, and it was back to school for Jack Holiday. Back to early bedtime and alarm clocks each morning. Back to trying to sit still while your mind fidgeted. Back to using arithmetic to cut up apple pies. It was back in school that dreams of go-carts, and clubhouses, and yes, even girls, helped pass the long hours.

It took a few days for things to get back to normal. But always for Jack, school grew tiresome again. Then on cold mornings, he would snuggle extra minutes under his warm blankets and pretend that he was captured by robbers and couldn't get out of bed because he was trapped. Mrs. Holiday usually spoiled that dream by calling a second time, always much louder.

During winter, Jack looked out the window to see if it could be a 'snow day' when school would be closed, but it never happened—not when he looked for it, anyway. Like the watched kettle that never boils, the weather never obeyed Jack's wishes. Sometimes he wondered if all kids everywhere would pray hard enough for a big snow storm, maybe they'd get some extra days off from school. This was devoutly to be wished for.

Now it was the first Tuesday of the New Year. The old calendar had been tossed in the trash and Jack was back in school. Today, Jack arrived early. Later, as getting to school got more difficult, he would grow careless and sometimes be tardy or just skinny-in under the bell.

Jack looked around the empty room. The tinsel, the sugar canes, the cutout Santas – all the decorations they had made for their Christmas party were gone. The scrubbed desks stood lined up like a regiment of soldiers. With a scent of pine-oil soap, the room was all scoured and shined and ready for the business end of dishing out education. Jack wandered up a row and found his own desk. Seeing the same old cluttered-up mess inside it made him feel more at home. He still had his stubby pencils, and the ball-point pen that didn't write, and the cock-eyed eraser that always smeared or chewed a hole in his paper. Going through some of his papers, Jack found one of his treasures, a note from Jennifer. Sometimes he thought of her quite a bit, and other times not at all. It was mostly when she was around that he thought about her. He hadn't seen her since school let out for vacation.

In a few minutes, Jack's classmates began to arrive in ones and twos and threes. The teacher, Ms. Rivera, was at her desk writing in her plan book. Rodney stood chatting at her elbow with his apple-polishing smile turned on full blast. Then Jack heard a voice behind him say:

"Hello, Jack."

Jack turned half hoping, half expecting to see Jennifer. Mary Jane came swirling up to Jack in a crinkly dress that rustled as she moved.

"Oh, hi, Mary Jane. New dress?"

"Uh, huh. I got it for Christmas. Do you like it?"

Jack always felt uncomfortable about being asked if he liked dresses, especially when asked while some of his classmates were looking on – classmates like Billy Suggs and his pals. Jack saw that Jennifer was looking, and that made it downright impossible to answer Mary Jane. If Jack said 'no', Mary Jane might not help him anymore if he got stuck on his homework. If he said 'yes', meaning he *liked* the dress, he'd probably end up getting the cold shoulder from Jennifer. This was the kind of tight spot that toasted Jack from his big toe clear up. The teacher's voice was never more welcome than it was just then.

"It's time. Take your seats, children." Ms. Rivera waited for all the children to sit down. Mary Jane didn't get a chance to hear what Jack thought about her new dress. He hurried back to his seat and, for once in his life, looked thankful about it.

"Hurry, Arthur, we're waiting," said the teacher. "Why is it taking you so long?"

"I are looking for my seat," said Arthur, in his own special way of speaking.

"That shouldn't be so difficult, Arthur. Everyone else is seated already."

Arthur sat down in an empty place and looked as happy as a bee in a blossom. The class looked at Ms. Rivera and back to Arthur and then back to the teacher again. Everyone knew that Arthur was sitting at the wrong desk.

"Arthur," said Ms. Rivera, folding her arms. "You're sitting in Sally's chair."

"I are?"

"Arthur, I think you meant to say, I AM!" corrected Ms. Rivera.

Arthur got a puzzled look on his face.

"You am? I thought *I* are," said Arthur. He looked inside the desk.

"Oh, never mind, Arthur. Just move up to the only desk that isn't occupied, please."

Arthur moved up to his own desk and whispered over to Fred, "I knew that other weren't my desk.

It weren't messy enough."

"Ms. Rivera! Ms. Rivera!" called Rodney, smiling fantastically and waving his hand in the air.

"Yes. What is it, Rodney?"

"Can I tell the class all I got for Christmas?"

"Not this morning, Rodney. We don't have time. Take out your math books, children."

# Holidays and Hoopla

Since Rodney was an only child of well to do parents, he bragged about his toys, in an effort to win friends. It didn't work. With all he owned, kids didn't like him much.

Jack was relieved the class didn't hear about Rodney's toys, especially his new chemistry set. As always, Jack hadn't started out to do anything wrong, but that's the way it turned out. He and Artie only wanted to improve the world by making a great invention through chemistry. They wanted to make a rocket, or a bomb, or something useful. Unfortunately, they'd never heard of the Geneva Convention and wound up discovering gas. What was intended to fill hearts with gladness, instead filled Rodney's house with a terrible odor which drove Rodney's mother's Bridge Club ladies outdoors in the cold of winter. The boy's concoction, without an air of exaggeration, was sickening. Its strength hung somewhere between a dog's mess, and a slab of limburger cheese.

The upshot was, Rodney and his parents had to stay overnight at a motel. Although the mixture was speedily tossed out, the smell lingered on. The house reeked so bad that Mrs. Van Skotus, Rodney's mother, had switched from carrying her nose so high to holding it tight. She refused to spend one more minute in the house until, as she put it, "their home was completely fumigated."

Naturally, Mrs. Van Skotus looked for someone to blame. Artie lived too many streets away to scold much. And, certainly, her precious Rodney could do no wrong. So, therefore, Jack got blamed for making what was probably the world's greatest stink bomb.

Later, stink bombs forgotten, Jack sat thinking, but not about his school work. He couldn't seem to fasten on that. His thoughts were on Jennifer. He wanted to walk her home again. He had no way of knowing whether her friendship toward him had cooled over the Christmas holiday. For that reason, it seemed to him just as difficult to ask her now as the first time. He wasn't all that sure about having a girlfriend, but somehow when he looked at Jennifer, things were different. He wanted to be with her, even though walking her home meant going way out of his way.

After school, Jack worked up his courage to ask Jennifer if he could walk her home. He dawdled by his locker as long as he thought he could without looking suspicious. Each time he was ready to ask her, she was surrounded by her girlfriends, and Jack found it too embarrassing to ask her in front of them. Finally, Jack saw that Jennifer had apparently made plans to walk home with Sue Lawson and Fatima Swarts. He was then all set to give up the idea entirely when he saw Fred leaving the school.

"Hey, Fred," called Jack.

"Huh? Oh, hi, Jack. I didn't see you behind me. What brings you in this direction?"

"Nothing special. Mind if I walk with you?"

"Heck no. I'm glad for the company. It'll be safer."

"Safer?" asked Jack.

"Yeah, I've got to watch out for a kid who calls himself Jasper." Fred looked from side to side as he spoke.

"Jasper? Who's he?"

"He's a punk. He's got a gang, you know. They call themselves the Rat Pack. Steer clear of them. They are strictly bad news. Say, you're not a friend of theirs, are you?"

"No. Why'd you ask?"

"I wouldn't want anything I said about them to get back."

Bundled in winter coats and smiles, children streamed from school. Some boarded school busses, others walked in small groups or by themselves. The sky was gray and quiet. The light coating of snow was brittle and wouldn't pack. Jack's feet slipped on the icy pavement as he walked. Fred took a running slide, followed by Jack.

"You still like Jennifer?"

"Aw, you know," said Jack, shrugging off the question while taking another slide on the ice. Jennifer was up ahead with her friends.

Fred had a glint of mischief in his eye. "Let's slide into the girls," he whispered.

A little voice inside Jack said 'no', but Fred's enthusiasm overruled it. The boys got back and took a running slide, which brought them skidding and bumping into Fatima, Sue, and Jennifer. The girls shrieked out loud. What became apparent was that they didn't much like being slid into, yet they didn't seem to mind some attention, either. The girl's faint grumblings seemed to egg the boys on. Still, Jack was not proud of himself. His little voice kept saying 'no'.

Sue had the worst time scrimmaging on the ice. Of the three girls, she was the featherweight. Her friends nicknamed her 'Toothpicks', because she was so skinny. It was all she could do to keep on her feet, when the boys came sliding into them. Fatima Swarts was called 'Fats' for good reason. When Fred slid into her, he might better have slid into a tree trunk. She was a good match for Billy Sugg's cousin, 'Tubby'. True to Newton's third law of action, when Fred slid into Fatima, he bounced more than he bumped her.

The first slide stirred up a good deal of nervous giggling. But Jack, ignoring his little voice, was to regret the second. As it sometimes happens, little things can be overdone. The next time, things were carried too far, or rather *Jennifer* was carried too far. Jack got too much of a running start and went sprawling in the snow with Jennifer. By the time her skirt flew and her feet had left the ground, she had lost more than her balance. It was obvious that she had lost her sense of humor as well.

Jack, blushing red as a fire truck, helped Jennifer pick up her scattered school books and tried to brush the snow off her coat.

"Gee, I'm sorry Jennifer. I didn't mean to…" Jack's apology trailed off to nothing, as it met an icy wall of silence.

Regaining her feet and her belongings, Jennifer turned her back on Jack and rejoined her friends, but not without uttering a scathing rebuke that made Jack blench and wither inside.

"Jack Holiday! I'll never speak to you again."

Once again, without meaning to, Jack had blundered. Walking home after that, he was sorry he hadn't listened to his little voice, for he knew that his last slide had been one slip too many.

## CHAPTER XVII

# Knight Errant

Monday morning when Jack opened his eyes, he pressed his nose against the cold bedroom window and peered out. His breath fogged the glass, but there was no hiding the cold, cottony world outside. His entire neighborhood was blanketed in deep snow for as far as his eyes could see.

Jack woke his younger brother, Peedie, and they got dressed. His sister Nancy had to be called twice. She hated to get out from under her nice warm covers. It wasn't long before they had bolted their breakfast and were ready to leave for school.

"Peedie," said Mrs. Holiday, "How come your toes are pointing out like that?"

"I don't know," said Peedie, looking down. "My feet were on straight when I got up this morning."

"Aw, Peedie's got his boots on backwards, Mom," said Jack. "He's got the right one on the left foot and the left on the right."

"Oh, I should have known," said Mrs. Holiday. "Which reminds me. You'll find a pair of mittens stuffed in the pockets of your coats. Now, I *do* hope you'll be very careful and not lose them right off."

"You ought to be happy we're not octopuses, Mom."

"Why, Jack?"

"Then you'd have to worry about losing eight mittens instead of just two."

"Worrying about two is enough for me, thank you," said Mrs. Holiday. "And please keep track of your hats and boots and scarves. It's expensive to buy winter clothes, you know."

Minutes later, they were making tracks up the street toward school.

Peedie's breath came out in white clouds of vapor. "Whoosh! Whoosh!" blew Peedie. "Look at me, Jack. Whoosh! Whoosh! I'm smoking."

"You look nutty enough without smoking," said Jack.

Soon, they reached school, separated, and headed toward their own classrooms. As children entered the building, they stamped the snow off their boots. Those who walked to school had cherry-tipped noses and rosy cheeks. Rodney came in looking like he was dressed for the North Pole, although he always got a ride to school, typically. Fred took off his coat and walked over to Jack.

"Has Jennifer spoken to you since that day?" asked Fred.

"What day?"

"The day you bowled her over on the ice."

"Oh, that day," remembered Jack glumly.

"Some girls can sure hold a grudge, can't they?"

"Yeah," said Jack. "That was on account of you, ya clown. You're the one that thought up sliding into the girls in the first place."

"What's the matter with doing that? Some girls like you for doing it," said Fred, arching his eyebrows as cocksure as a salesman. Jack was almost as sure that girls didn't like that, and said so.

"Okay Fred. If you're so smart, tell me one girl that'd like you for knocking her down," said Jack, ready to argue the point. "Go ahead. Just name one."

Fred got a look on his face like he was holding all the aces. "That's easy," he said. "Fatima Swarts."

Fred's answer stopped Jack cold. He had to admit that Fatima liked Fred, and maybe even more so since he'd slid into her. For some reason, a guy could whack Fatima over the head and she'd take a liking to him. It just made Jack more vexed about the whole female race. Admitting that Fred had bested him with that argument, all Jack could say was: "Girls! Phooey!"

Rodney sauntered over to where Jack was standing, and stood grinning at him.

"What do you want, Rodney?"

"My mother says she thinks your family should pay for the stink bomb that ruined her Bridge party."

Jack looked at Rodney with amazement. He wondered how Rodney could say such a thing in all seriousness, and still keep a silly smile on his face.

"What do you mean, pay for it? We all played with your chemistry set, even you."

"It was your idea, so it's your fault."

"You're impossible, Rodney."

"Nevertheless, my mother says you've got to pay for it. When you do something wrong, you've got to pay for it."

The bell rang and ended the discussion. The boys went to their desks. It was one time Jack was happy to stop talking, at least talking with Rodney. Ms. Rivera took attendance, Sue led the Pledge of Allegiance, and school began. Even during arithmetic, Jack couldn't get Rodney and the stink bomb off his mind.

*What a kid,* he thought. *Where did he get all his screwy ideas, anyway? I should pay for the stink bomb?* Anytime anything happened at Rodney's, it was always someone else's fault. As much as he wanted to forget about the whole matter, it kept running through his mind. When a worry got in Jack's mind, he just couldn't shake it.

Why was it whenever he played with Rodney or Rodney's things, Jack always wound up getting in trouble? Why did things just keep happening one after the other where he'd get the blame? Why did things happen that he hadn't intended to happen? Like knocking Jennifer over? If he had the power to cause good things to happen, he would have built himself a clubhouse by now. Jack was getting tired wracking his brain over things when he felt a tap on his shoulder. It was Fred.

"Sst!" Fred whispered. "Here's a note for you. It was passed to me."

Jack took the scrap of paper and looked around him. Ms. Rivera was busy testing Artie on his arithmetic facts at the front of the room. Jack didn't know who could be sending him a message. The paper was folded into triangles and crackled loudly when he opened it. He looked again to see if anyone was watching. His hand trembled slightly with anticipation. Could it be a message from Rodney demanding payment for stink bomb damage? No, the handwriting was even neater than Rodney's. Jack looked at the signature at the bottom. It was signed simply with one big initial, a capital "J".

Jack looked across the aisle toward Jennifer. Catching her eye, Jennifer looked away. Jack returned to the note and read it:

*Jack,*
   *Will you walk me home after school? I'm scared to walk home because of some mean bullies.*

Jack pored over the note several times, feeling more chivalrous each time he read it. Could Sir Lancelot do any less for his Lady Guinevere? Of course, Jack would be Jennifer's shining knight. Of course, he would walk her home and be her protector.

Jack pondered over how he would answer Jennifer's note in a proper dignified manner, and with all the right sentiment, and with his miserable scrawly handwriting. He finally settled for an undramatic "yes" added to the bottom of her note. He passed it back to her.

Jennifer read the simple answer and, with a look that could melt the wings off a wax candle angel, smiled at Jack with her eyes. Jack's dream life was so great after that, he could hardly think about his school work.

In the cafeteria, Fred sat beside Jack. Fred was the first to speak: "So, you're going to walk Jennifer home?" he said between mouthfuls.

"You read my note, huh?"

"Even if I hadn't read it, I could have guessed. Don't forget to watch out for Jasper. His real name is Casper, but he doesn't let anybody call him that, except his mother and the teacher at his school. A kid I know told me."

"His name is Casper, but he calls himself Jasper?"

"Yeah, take my word for it, Jack, stay away from him. He's a mean kid. He lives near Jennifer's neighborhood and has a gang, and bullies all the kids. I think he kinda likes Jennifer, but she doesn't like him. *None* of the kids like him much. They're all pretty afraid of him."

Jack hardly noticed the afternoon pass. He was excited about walking Jennifer home again. After school, Peedie met Jack at his locker.

"Peedie, you walk home with Nancy or some of the other kids."

"How come, Jack?"

"I got a few things to do before I head home."

"Do you have to stay after school?"

"No, not tonight."

"Can't I come with you?"

"No. Just head on home. I'll be along in a while." Jack was beginning to grow annoyed with Peedie for hanging around and asking so many questions. "Will you get along, Peedie, please?"

Peedie looked up at Jack suspiciously as Jack was keeping himself buried in his locker, hoping for Peedie to disappear.

Peedie thought for a minute and finally said:

"You going to walk a girl home, Jack?"

"Peedie, why are you so nosy?"

"Well, are you?"

"Peedie, it's none of your business."

Jack started pushing Peedie down the hall toward the outside door.

"Why don't you like Mary Jane, Jack? She likes you."

"For gosh sakes, why should I like Mary Jane?"

"Well, for one thing, she lives on our street."

"Peedie, you're too young to know anything about girls. Just tell Mom I'll be home in a little while and don't say anything more." Jack saw Peedie out the door and returned to meet Jennifer at her locker. They left the building by a different entrance.

Outside, Jack pulled on his red and black checkered hunting cap, then walked beside Jennifer. He didn't notice the cold, or the slippery pavement, or any discomfort whatever. He was oblivious to everything. Some of the children were climbing the piles of snow and jumping in the snowdrifts. They seemed young and silly to Jack, who was enjoying Jennifer's company and feeling ten feet tall.

"Who are the bullies that you wrote about in your note, Jennifer?"

"They're awful, Jack. Just awful. Especially the one that's called Jasper."

"What do they do?"

"Oh, sometimes they've knocked our books out of our hands. And this morning they threw icy snowballs at some of us girls as we walked by. They're the worst boys in the world. Uh, oh,...don't look now. They're across the street."

"Where?"

"On the corner. But don't look at them, Jack, maybe they won't notice us."
Jennifer pulled her coat collar up.

Jack couldn't help sneaking a glance across at the three boys who were standing
on the corner. They had on black leather jackets, black boots, tight pants, and no hats.
Jack had never seen any boys like them in his neighborhood. He was grateful they
didn't seem to be paying any attention to Jennifer or himself.

All too soon, Jack had seen Jennifer safely to her door and said goodbye. It had
been at least a dozen weeks since he had walked Jennifer home by himself. He'd
almost forgotten how nice it was.

The air was still brisk, but he didn't notice the cold at all, not with the picture of
Jennifer in his mind. The world seemed a wonderful place. The snow scrunched
under his boots as he walked. Jack was smiling to himself, and he usually didn't do
that.

He was so delighted with the thought of Jennifer, that he had no thought of
looking ahead of him. Suddenly, and with a shudder that he could not even explain to
himself, he looked up. Approaching him on the icy sidewalk were the three leather-
jacketed boys.

Edging the sidewalk were high piles of snow where it had been pushed aside by the plow. The three boys formed a solid wall across the entire sidewalk. Someone would have to move into the piled snow for them to pass by each other. They blocked Jack's way home.

Jack didn't want to look at them. He only wanted to pass. But as they met, the boys stopped and blocked him. He was forced to look into their leering faces. He could tell that they were blocking his way on purpose. He wondered what they were up to and what he should do next.

CHAPTER XVIII

# Bully Initiation

The boy in the center had a snarly, piggy face. The boy standing at his right was rat-faced and had greasy hair. The third was plain, except that he had mossy-green teeth like he never brushed them. Jack moved to pass, but they blocked his way. The piggy-faced boy was obviously the leader and also was the first to speak.

"Lookit the lover boy. Ain't he fancy? Whatcher name? Ask him what's his name, Luke," said Piggy-face to Rat-face.

"Dontcha know your name, kid?"

Jack only nodded. He didn't trust them. Still, he didn't want to ask for trouble. He was trying to figure a way out.

"Whatsa matter, cat got your tongue? Whatcher name? Say it." said the piggy-faced boy.

"My name is Jack."

"His name is Jack. Ain't that cute? Don't you think that name's cute, Matt?" The mossy-toothed kid snickered and slapped his pant leg. The rat-faced boy smirked. "S'funny, I thought a 'jack' was a thing ya used to lift a car. Ya know what my name is, er, Jerk?"

Jack shook his head.

"I think Jerk fits him better'n Jack, don't you, Luke? So ya don't know my name, huh? Ya better learn it, Jerk. My name's Jasper, Jasper Scufflaw. Don't you ever forget it, see. I'm boss of this block.

"Boss!" sneered Jasper. "Ain't you ever heerd of a boss? Head man, top guy, boss! What I say goes, see?"

Jasper thumped his leather-jacketed chest while Jack was looking for some way to get away from him and his creepy sidekicks, but he didn't see how he could.

"Let's initiate 'im," said Rat-face.

"Yeah, let's," said the one with the rotten teeth.

"Those are pretty mitties you got there. Hold 'em out so we can see 'em, Jerk."

Jack held his hands out part way and Jasper grabbed his fingers.

"Down, Jerk! Get down on your knees. Get down on your knees and beg!"

While Jack squirmed, the boy called Luke snatched Jack's red and black checkered cap.

"Lookit this, boss. He was going hunting with this here hunting cap. Ain't that a scream. Him hunting on our block."

"You saw that pigeon he walked home, din't ya," said Jasper.

111

Jack slipped his hands out of his mittens before Jasper was able to twist his fingers any further. Jasper, the boy that Fred and Jennifer had warned him about, was left holding the gloves. Jack could now feel his heart pounding and blood throbbing through his temples.

"Give me that hat!" said Jack.

"Hear that, boss? He wants his hat and he din't even say please."

"Whatsa matter? Ain't ya got no manners, Jerk?"

Jack tried to grab the hat from the greasy haired one. But before he could get hold of it, Luke tossed it to Matt.

"Here it is. Come and get it, Jerk."

Just as Jack had almost reached him, "Mossy" tossed it over his head back to Rat-face calling, "Catch, Luke. We'll have to learn Jerk here some manners."

Jack jumped and his hand ticked his cap as it was thrown over his head. It landed short, skittering over the icy sidewalk. He almost reached it when "Mossy" stuck out his foot and tripped him, sending him sprawling on the ice. Jasper got to it first and was able to grab it up before Jack.

"Lookit that, boss. Jerk ain't learned to walk yet." laughed Luke.

The ice was cold and should have stung Jack's bare hands, but he didn't notice it. He was shaking, but not from the cold. He felt scared and foolish sprawled out on the pavement.

"Ya know who the boss is now, dontcha, Jerk?" Jasper, his fists propped on his hips, stood looking down at Jack. Jack wanted to call him a big creep, but he knew that creeps hate being called creeps.

Jack got to his feet. Surrounded by the leather jackets, he felt time itself stood still. He began to feel shivery. The air was much crisper than it had been earlier when he had walked Jennifer home from school. His hair was mussed up and snow clung to the front of his coat. He saw people walking down the other side of the street on their way to stores and elsewhere. It seemed to Jack that they walked quickly; appearing as if they were a great distance off.

"Jerky looks sick. Don't you think Jerky looks sick, Luke? Better fix 'im an ice bag for his head." Jasper flipped the hat over to Luke.

I gitcha, boss." Luke stooped over and started to scoop snow into Jack's hat. Jack dashed at Luke and, while wrestling him for the hat, swung Luke around, causing him to topple into Jasper and knock him off balance. Jasper caught himself and didn't fall.

"Why ya stupid clown. I don't know why I keep dumb clunks like you in my gang." Jasper socked the rat-faced kid hard in the arm.

A man in an overcoat was walking toward them on the sidewalk. He didn't seem to notice them in particular, but he gave Jack an idea. While Jasper and Luke were wrangling, Jack decided to make a desperate try for freedom. He would pretend to know the man and call to him. Then with the attention drawn away from himself, Jack would make a dash between Jasper and Luke.

"Hi, Mr. Smith," called Jack. Jasper and Luke turned and looked at the approaching man. Jack ran. He might have made it, but "Mossy", behind him, cried out:

"Jasper! Jerky's trying to lamb!"

So "Mossy" cheated Jack out of his race for freedom. The jacketed goons grabbed Jack and held him. The man in the overcoat approached, passed, but then walked on.

"Take holt of Jerk's arm, Matt," said Jasper.

They held Jack pinned between them. Jack wanted to kick and scratch, but he'd always been taught to fight fair.

"Jerk, here, don't like our company, boss," said Luke.

"Yah, Jerk's got bad manners. 'Gonna leave us without saying goodbye first. Keep aholt of him." Jack struggled, but it was no use, because they had his arms twisted behind him. Jasper bent down and picked up some snow.

"We gotta get Jerk washed clean a his bad manners."

Jasper tried to push snow in Jack's face, but he turned his head from side to side. Jasper grabbed Jack by the hair, tugged his head back, and mashed the snow in his face.

"Boss, I think you learned him good enough. Don't you?"

"Okay, Matty. He knows who's boss now, dontcha, Jerky? Ya see I got a very warm heart, don't I, boys? But when someone blocks me or don't give me proper respeck, there's only one thing for me to do – learn 'im. Ain't that right, boys?"

"Should we let him go now, boss?"

"Sure, let 'im loose."

The second Luke and Matt let go of Jack's arms, Jasper, without any warning, punched Jack hard in the stomach. As Jack doubled up, Jasper butted him back into a snowbank.

"Okay boys. Let's shove off." Jasper started up the street with his stooges. "That was just a reminder for 'im. Remember, Jerk, if ya don't want it to go rough on ya, you remember who the boss is here."

Jasper glared back over his shoulder. "Think of Jasper, Jasper Scufflaw."

Jack picked himself up out of the snow pile. He didn't even notice the snow that he had clenched in his bare fists. Within him raged a storm. He wanted to lash out at Jasper and his goons, but he felt powerless against them. In his agitation, he packed the snow into a snowball. Jasper and his followers were about twenty feet away when Jack called after them in the mushiest voice he could:

"Oh Casper! Cass-purr!"

The three boys turned. A dumb look of surprise came over the faces of Luke and Matt, but Jasper's face curdled and became more vicious than before. At first, the three just stood as if their right to bluster and bully had never before been challenged.

"Don't just stand there like dumbbells. Get 'im! Get the Jerk!" snarled Jasper.

The boys, led by Jasper, began to run toward Jack. He let fly with the snowball that he'd hard-packed. Jasper ducked and it hit Luke in the knee. Jack snapped up his hat and ran. The boys had already reached the place where the mittens were, so Jack had to leave them behind. He ran and ran, with Jasper and his henchmen pounding after him like stampeding cattle. He ran like he'd never run before. He was scared, but he was running fast and he was running free.

He didn't know when Jasper's hoodlums gave up the chase. They had run their best, but he had outrun them. He found himself alone uptown. He gasped for air. If he ached, he didn't feel it. Now he noticed a few shoppers who scurried by. The stores were brightly lit up. In the air, light flecks of snow drifted slowly down. As he passed by the bright window displays, he stared at them. He wondered at their cheer, in view of his horrible experience with Jasper's gang.

114

Wait till he told his dad about them, he thought – just wait. Soon he was home. Mother greeted him at the door.

Jack felt the whole grief of it well up in him. Tears began to flood his eyes. He tried to explain what had happened, but his words seemed to leap over each other as he was trying to explain it all in a single breath. And it only came out a jumble. Just then, Mr. Holiday entered the kitchen and asked what was wrong.

"Jack has been trying to tell me something about some boys who stopped him on the way home. They punched him and tore his hat."

Mr. Holiday listened while Jack spilled out the whole story. When Jack had finished, a charged stillness filled the air while Mr. Holiday aimlessly tapped his newspaper against his knee.

"Try to forget it, son," he said finally. "It's too bad it happened, but it's all over now."

"But, Dad," said Jack in astonishment. "Aren't…aren't you going to do anything?"

"There have always been bullies, and there probably always will be." Mr. Holiday shrugged his shoulders and moved off to the living room with his newspaper. Jack followed him.

"But why did they pick on me? I never had anything to do with them. Shouldn't a kid like Jasper be locked up so he'll know better?"

"Jack, nobody can be forced to know better." Mr. Holiday sat down in his chair and opened his paper.

"But, Dad, how come some kids follow a bully like Jasper?"

"Who knows?" said Mr. Holiday, not looking up from his paper. "Perhaps getting bossed around and being part of a gang keeps them from feeling like nobodies." Mr. Holiday turned to another page.

"Jack," called Mrs. Holiday from the kitchen. "I've baked some fresh chocolate chip cookies. Come have one before Nancy and Peedie eat them all up."

A delicious aroma of fresh baked cookies entered the room.

"No thanks," mumbled Jack, as he headed up to his room.

CHAPTER XIX

# Bridge to Artie's House

It was cold – ear-frosting, toe-stinging cold. It was hard to understand how the middle of February could be colder than it had been in December. But this day it was. And the sun was shining, too – shining through snowflakes. It was clearly muddle-headed weather. Jack pushed into the Kmart through the big glass doors. He was shopping for valentines. It was Monday, but there was no school because of Lincoln's birthday.

Jack walked down an aisle between counters piled with stacks of merchandise. Near the door was the candy counter with its glass covered bins. There were mints of all colors of the rainbow, jelly beans, candy bars, chewing gum, light and dark chocolates like fancy buttons, and candy kisses wrapped in tinfoil. There was a bellyache full of sweets to drool over.

Another counter was loaded with bottles, jars, and cans of hair tonic, shampoo, face cream, perfume – all colors, all prices, all smells. At the end of this counter was a jewelry display. Earrings for $1.98, pins for $0.79, bracelets for $0.89. The next counter was a sewing counter. Skeins of yarn and spools of thread by the mile lined the shelf. Zippers and buttons, all shapes and sizes. Piles and piles of stuff all packaged, priced, and clamoring for attention. Displays that dazzled the eye like a kaleidoscope.

Finally, Jack found the greeting card counter. A special display had been set up for valentines. The counter was as long as an automobile. It was stacked with hearts and hearts and more hearts. Red hearts, frilly hearts, shiny hearts. Hearts both big and small. Each card with its own special way of saying "Be My Valentine." Each message had its own slant: comic or sentimental, friendly or romantic. Fifteen, thirty-five, even seventy-five cents each, depending on how large and fancy.

Jack knew he would be buying a card for everyone in his class, and one for the teacher. Most of the cards he picked out were the plain kind, not mushy at all. Some were sporty with messages like "You're my baseball, Valentine, get the pitch?" This one was right for a good buddy. Other cards were for laughs. And some even poked fun and had a sting to them.

Then there was a special selection of cards of the romantic kind. Cards that meant business. Cards with sayings such as, "Sweetheart, wont you be my Valentine?" This kind made Jack blush. They made him think long and deep thoughts. Would he dare give Jennifer one of these, and should he? It took him a long time to make up his mind. Apparently, she had forgiven him for the sliding incident. She was more friendly since he had walked her home and protected her from the bullies. Did she really like Jack best? Or was she only toying with him? He couldn't be sure. Why were girls so mysterious?

After Jack bought all his valentines, he pushed back out into the cold street air. He had just crossed at the traffic signal when he heard his name called.

"Hey, Jack. Wait up."

Jack looked around and saw Billy Suggs running to catch up with him.

After Billy caught up and caught his breath, too, he said:

"Are you going to Artie's place?"

"No. I was just at the Kmart. Why'd you ask?"

"Oh, I'm just heading to Artie's, myself. You know the basketball game we got coming up with the class across the hall? Well, we're going to work up some special plans. If you're not doing anything, why don't you come along."

"Who else will be there?"

"Just Artie, Rodney, myself, and maybe some others. How about it? You want to come, too?"

"Sure. I haven't anything else to do."

As they walked along the snow-packed sidewalk, Jack remembered the last time he'd been uptown. It was just after walking Jennifer home. He didn't like to think about it. The memory was still too painful, so he didn't tell Billy about the awful Jasper gang.

"Where does Artie live, anyhow?" asked Jack.

"Just past Creek Street. Haven't you ever been to his place?"

Jack had to shake his head 'no'. There were a lot of homes of kids in his class that he'd never visited. Lots of kids had never been to his house, either. It was almost like exploring to go see what exciting things other kids had in their neighborhoods. He liked to see what toys and games they might have, too.

"Let's take the shortcut to his place, okay?"

"Sure, why not," answered Jack. Jack knew they must be nearing Artie's because they were on Creek Street and he could hear the creek gurgling up ahead. He'd been on the street before, but mostly when riding by in the family car. Suddenly, Billy broke away and ran down a small incline toward the creek. Jack was surprised, but not at Billy, for Billy was always full of little tricks. As far as Jack could figure, Billy had disappeared behind a big tree at the creek bank. When Jack reached the tree and peeked around, he was astonished to find that the tree was hollow and Billy was standing inside it grinning like everything.

"Boo! Fooled you, didn't I?" said Billy, still grinning like mad. "Isn't this tree neat?"

Jack had to agree that it was the neatest tree he'd ever seen. Billy didn't stop at that, because he was bubbling over to show something else. He hurried on not waiting for Jack. He ran toward the creek. Jack was beginning to wonder if he would have to walk on ice or something. Billy was just cram full of goofy ideas.

When Jack looked next, Billy was bounding up a ramp that led onto the strangest bridge Jack had ever seen. It was made of wire cable and planking strung between some not-too-sturdy looking wood poles. The poles were embedded in each side of the creek bank. Billy was standing near the center of the bridge where it sagged the most, and was waving wildly to Jack to hurry and follow him.

The bridge spanned the steep creek banks like a giant spider web. The upper two cables served both as support, and as handrails. The board walkway was as narrow as a footpath and was strictly a footbridge. Jack could see that, for it was no wider than a fat dog. Jack looked down through the cracks in the planking. The turbulent creek water rushing underneath dizzied his head.

He should have expected it. Billy was not a boy to miss a trick. When he was just safely to mid-center, Billy started to jump up and down, shaking the whole bridge! Jack had to grab for the cable to hold on. With Billy jumping, the bridge whipped and bounced like a runaway jump rope.

"Hey, you clown! You nearly made me drop my valentines," said Jack, feeling like a Jack-In-The- Box as the bridge bobbed under him.

Billy laughed like crazy. He enjoyed the pitching, lurching, swaying motion. "Haven't you ever been on this before?" he said, laughing.

"No, what's it called?" said Jack, still hanging on for his life.

"This is the Old Swinging Bridge. Isn't this a neat shortcut?"

Jack had to agree that the name was suitable, although everything joggled before his eyes.

A few minutes later, after walking a way along the creek bank, Billy stopped and pointed up. Through the bare, twisted, and dark-trunk trees, Jack could see an old house perched on the edge of the steep hill. It looked like a weathered, termite-eaten tree stump stripped of its bark.

"That's Artie's house." said Billy.

The boys then started to climb the steep ascent of roots, rocks, and rusted tin cans, caked over with ice and snow. It was difficult climbing. The snow underfoot caused their feet to slip, and it was necessary to lean to the bank to keep their balance. Sometimes, they were forced to grab a root or hold onto a branch to prevent skidding downhill altogether. As they drew near Artie's house, Jack noticed that the window panes were like tic-tac-toe frames, an impression that was aided by the crossed tape patches over cracks in the glass. Reaching the top of the bank, Jack saw, scattered about the yard, pieces of rusty scrap iron and piles of old lumber. A junk automobile without wheels clung to the brink of the bank as if it had struggled there, crawled to a halt, and would never move again.

"Artie lives *here*?" asked Jack.

"Sure thing. Isn't it neat? Sometimes we play cops and robbers in that old jalopy."

Soon they came to the side of the house. Billy opened an old screen door, knocked, and then closed it. When they got no answer, he had to do it again. After what seemed like a long wait, the door swung open and an unshaven man looked out through the rusted holes in the screen door. The room behind the man looked like a kitchen.

"What do you want?" asked the man, a little gruffly.

"Is Artie here?" asked Billy.

Without answering, the man turned and called: "Artie. Some kids are here to see you."

Soon, Artie came to the door and invited them in. Cracked linoleum on the floor had big swatches where the pattern had completely worn away. Billy and Jack took off their boots and left them by the door.

"Follow me. I are been working on the secret plans for the game Friday."

"What have you done, Artie, worked out some new plays?" asked Jack. It was hard for him to feel natural in such a strange place. Everything in the house seemed to be droopy, even the floor. Jack got to thinking more and more about the whole works sliding into the creek.

"Wait and we'll show you," said Billy with a secret little smile.

Then Artie brought out a piece of paper and handed it to Jack. Artie couldn't hide his pleasure over it. Jack sat down on an old day bed that sagged in the middle like a swayback horse. He tipped the paper till the most light fell on it, and then read it to himself. On the paper was written:

| | |
|---|---|
| *Friday the 13ᵗʰ* | *bad luck* |
| *Brake mear* | *bad luck* |
| *Black cat cross path* | *bad luck* |
| *Four leaf clover* | *good luck* |
| *Find a penny* | *good luck* |
| *Step on crack* | *bad luck* |
| *Walk under lader* | *bad luck* |

After Jack finished reading what Billy and Artie had written on the paper, he must have had a dumb look on his face. He certainly was speechless. He looked back to the paper to see if he might have overlooked something on the other side which might explain what it was all about. Finally, all he could do was shake his head.

"What's the matter," asked Billy. "Don't you get it?"

"I guess not. What's this got to do with our basketball game on Friday?"

"It are everything to do with it," said Artie rather impatiently.

"Wait, Artie. Let me try and explain it to Jack," said Billy. "You know, of course, that luck has a lot to do with how things turn out, don't you?"

"I suppose so."

"Well, Artie, me, and Rodney are working out this list of things of good luck and bad luck so we can win the game Friday. For instance, things that are bad luck we're going to avoid, or sic onto the other team. Good luck we're collecting for *our* side. Do you get it now?"

"I think so. How can you tell what's good luck or bad luck?" asked Jack, still looking puzzled.

"That's just what we're working on now. We're looking through books and encyclopedias to get all the true facts on all kinds of luck, so we can make our list the best possible for the game. So far, most of the things we've found are bad luck, but we hope to even it up."

Just then, Artie saw Rodney at the door and went to the kitchen to let him in. When Rodney came in he was dripping wet.

"Rodney," said Jack. "What happened to your coat and stuff?"

Rodney rolled up his muddy pant legs. "Didn't Billy tell you how we're going to avoid bad luck so we can win the game Friday?"

"Yeah, he did," said Jack. "What's that got to do with you getting all slopped up like that?"

"Well, it was like this," said Rodney, pinching up his face so that his smile twisted. "As I started to come over the swinging bridge, I jumped over a crack and ..."

At this point, Rodney stopped and swallowed as if it took courage to finish his story.

"Then what?" prodded Jack.

"Oh, don't worry. I didn't step on any crack. But jumping over one, I slipped and slid down the bank into the creek. That's how I got muddy."

Billy and Artie looked amazed. Jack could have laughed, but he didn't. He could see that the boys were pretty serious about this good and bad luck business.

CHAPTER XX

# Valentines and Lucky Charms

The night before Valentine's Day in the Holiday household was always a thought-tugging time with a little giggling thrown in. The giggling part came from some of the funny sayings on the valentines. The thoughtful part was who to match-up with which cards. Matching cards to friends always had to be done carefully and privately, even by little Peedie.

"You going to give Suzy *this* one?" Jack said to Peedie, holding up a particularly gushy love-and-kisses kind of valentine. Jack thought that this comment would irk his little brother, and he guessed right.

"Her?! No, I'm going to give her this baboon card," said Peedie.

"Oh, I thought she was your girlfriend," teased Jack.

Peedie would have thrown something had he had anything to throw. As it was, his anger quickly passed in getting back to the job of writing names on his cards. Hunched over the coffee table in the living room with his cards spread all around him, and the TV going full blast, Peedie worked on his valentines like a monk decorating a manuscript. All that was missing was the sacred robe and skull cap. Even without his front teeth, he had a firm bite on his tongue which, by the seventh card, he'd nearly bitten through. He squeezed his pencil with a tiger's grip that turned his knuckles white.

Jack looked over to see what he might tease his sister, Nancy, about. As an experienced old hand at making out valentines, she had her work well-covered and hidden from Jack's prying eyes. She'd suffered enough of his taunts to expect the worst, and was no slouch in dishing out a few digs herself when the situation called for it. This created a balance of power in the touchy department of friendships, or, more precisely, "romances".

Jack had a big decision to make. He had picked out one very special card. It was lacy with a real satin heart in the center of it. It was the most expensive card he had bought. Far more than the money spent was the affection invested in the card. This was the kind of card that took real courage to give. If Jack gave Jennifer this extra special card, she would know he was serious. It was bound to stand out like a tree in a desert. Jennifer would have to love it, snub it, or laugh at it. A card this fancy just couldn't be ignored. Jack had some extra cards, just in case he changed his mind, or his nerve gave out before he gave her the card.

The next day, Jack, Nancy, and Peedie packed up their valentines and trotted off to school. After Jack had hung up his coat, he entered the classroom. At the back of

122

the room on the reading table was a big box covered with white paper that had red paper hearts all over it. On the top of the box was a big slot like a mailbox ready to receive their cards.

Jack looked down the aisle between the desks like it was the longest walk he'd ever have to take. With every step, he knew he could change his mind. As he walked toward the valentine box, it loomed even larger before his eyes. The box was surrounded by a circle of early-watch birds who were making remarks as valentines were dropped in the slot.

Jack could still change his mind, but only with some tricky maneuver. A card held back from the box would be sure to draw notice and comment. Now he stood before the box, his heart thumping. It was his last chance to change his mind. Jack stuffed all his valentines into the box.

All through school that day, Jack kept pondering over the situation. The party was to be held the last period of the day, when the cards would be handed out and refreshments served. To change his mind now would mean he would have to somehow get the card out of the box. This was hardly possible since the box now swelled by the hundreds. Jack began to wonder whether it might not have been better to sign the special card for Jennifer with something safe like "Guess who?" or "From your secret admirer," instead of his signature. It was too late to change now. The arrow had been shot and there was no reversing it.

Jack was still deep in thought when it came time for the party. And Billy and Artie came over to visit him.

"Hi, Jack."

"Oh, hi Billy. Hi Artie. Say, have you made any plans for practicing basketball? I've heard that the team across the hall has had five practices already, and plans to put in several more before the big game Friday."

"Relax, buddy boy. There's nothing to worry about," said Billy puffing up like a grouse as he winked at Artie. We've got this one in the bag. Isn't that right, Artie?"

"It sure are."

"I don't know how you can be so sure. I hear they've got some pretty good players," said Jack.

"So, what." Billy looked both ways and then whispered in Jack's ear. "Don't forget, luck'll be on our side."

"But don't you think we should practice anyhow? Just to be sure?"

"Listen," said Billy. "I couldn't be anymore sure than I am now. Believe me, we'll have all the luck on our side. We're bound to win. We've got some super magic that – if you'll pardon me saying it – has been practiced and proved through the ages. Tell him about it Artie."

"It's like this, Jack. We read up and found out which things is charms and which things is taboos. Charms is lucky pieces and medals and stuff that gives good luck to them that holds them. Taboos is things not to do because they bring bad luck. For instance, some words is taboo because saying 'em brings bad luck."

"What are the bad luck words, Artie?" asked Jack.

"Umm!" gulped Artie, getting a bug-eyed, flustered look on his face, and turning to Billy for help.

"Billy, how can I tell Jack the bad luck words? If I are to say them, then I might get jinxed."

Just at that moment, the passing of refreshments and valentines began, so Artie didn't have to figure a way out of his weird word problem. Billie and Artie returned to their desks while Jack sat down at his own to begin opening his valentines, and nibble at his party treats. One of the first cards Jack opened was a gaudy, frilly thing with a rosy bare cupid in the center of a big heart shooting arrows. For a minute, his heart leaped. Then he turned the card over and saw two neat initials – 'M.J'. There was only one M.J. he could think of – Mary Jane. At that moment, the thought that she might be looking his way kept Jack from looking *her* way. If anything, Jack sank lower in his seat. Then Fred came to the rescue by showing Jack a funny Snoopy valentine. And they chuckled over it together. Jack hid the M.J. valentine in his desk.

During all the laughing and talking, Jack sneaked a look in Jennifer's direction. His hunch was right. Jennifer was sitting before her pile of valentines, and she had just opened Jack's! It was one of those moments that are engraved on the memory forever, like a living monument. Faces sometimes say more than words. The look on Jennifer's face spoke eloquently and straight to his heart. It stirred Jack so much, that had he been butter, he would have melted. He forgot all about the rest of the party. A sweet look from Jennifer could put him up in the clouds faster than a rocket.

After the party was over, Billy, Artie, and Rodney came over to Jack's desk, bringing with them a sack. At first, Jack couldn't quite understand what they were talking about. The coming basketball game had slipped completely from his mind.

"Here's what you might call our secret weapons," said Billy, plunking the sack down on Jack's desk.

"Secret weapons?" said Jack with surprise.

"For our basketball game Friday. You haven't forgotten already have you? We were just talking about it."

"Oh yeah. What have you got in there?"

"Careful. Don't talk too loud. We wouldn't want our secret to get out."

Billy reached down in the sack, while Rodney and Artie crowded by his side like a couple of proud parents. The first thing Billy clunked on the desk was a horseshoe.

"This is one of our strong, good luck charms. Be sure to hold it prongs up so the luck won't pour out."

Billy reached back into the bag and brought out a green stone and held it up to the light.

"What's that stone?" asked Jack.

"That are jade," said Artie, with a good deal of pride.

"What does jade do?"

"What does jade do?" said Billy, somewhat miffed at the question. "It's a magic stone for good luck. Of course, a garnet stone would be better because that guarantees power and victory, but we couldn't afford to buy one. Don't forget, though, we've collected many things here, and that'll give us big luck."

"Show him what I brought, Billy," said Rodney, who was getting restless because they were paying so much attention to a piece of jade. He was itching for them to get to *his* contribution.

Billy, beaming once more, dipped into the sack and brought out a fuzzy rabbit's foot on a keychain. Jack wanted to say that the rabbit's foot couldn't be very lucky because the rabbit had lost it, but he stopped himself. The boys were taking it much too seriously to see the humor in it.

Last of all, Billy brought out a dry, three-leaf clover and held it up gently between his finger and thumb. Jack looked at it with raised eyebrows.

"I thought that only four-leaf clovers were lucky ones. That one's only got three leaves."

"So, it has," said Billy. "The horseshoe or stone must have bumped it." Billy looked deep in the sack and came up with the missing leaf. "Have you got any glue? We'll paste it back together. Don't forget, either, this isn't all we got, you know. For instance, if your right eye itches, that's good luck. And we're all looking round to see if we can find a magic wand somewhere."

Looking down at the paltry good luck junk spread out on Jack's desk, a loss of excitement and confidence came over the boys that Billy felt he had to remedy with more words.

"Don't forget. It's not just lucky charms that'll give us good luck on the game Friday. It's staying away from taboo stuff, too. This week, don't spill any salt, break any mirrors, walk under any ladders, or let black cats cross your path."

The bell rang for the end of the school day and, in this case, the end of the party. All the children began gathering up their cards and all the candy that was left. Ms. Rivera was directing the clean-up committee in tidying the room. Jack started to glance in Jennifer's direction, when Rodney sneezed.

"For golly sakes, say 'Gesundheit' quick! You don't want to bring us bad luck, do you?" said Billy.

"Gesundheit," said Rodney. "I guess I caught a cold from getting wet in the creek at your place, Artie."

"Just don't forget to say 'Gesundheit' each time you sneeze," warned Billy.

"Right," said Rodney, sniffling and twitching his nose.

Jack wanted to say again that even with all their lucky charms, they should practice before the game. Before he could mention it, however, the boys had gone back to their own desks to gather their things and go home. Jack wasn't sorry, because his thoughts returned to Jennifer. He'd been quite brash and forward to give her such a fancy valentine after she'd been angry with him. Now, he was happy he'd given her the card. Only he wondered when he should speak to her. Before he made up his mind, he realized she was gone.

Jack dropped his things and scooted for the hall door. Shouldering his way through crowds of kids putting on their coats and boots, he saw that she'd already left her locker, had on her coat, and was rushing toward the outside door. Before leaving, she turned and glanced back at him. In that fleeting second before she closed the door, Jack was sure he saw tears in her eyes.

That stopped him in his tracks. Once he'd made her angry. Opening his valentine, she'd given him a look that had made his heart do handsprings. Now, did he make her cry? Jack slumped back to his locker shaking his head. He couldn't help wondering at all the mystery summed up in that one word – GIRLS!

## CHAPTER XXI

# The Basketball Hex

Jack always knew when he had reached the locker room. Without hearing locker doors slam, or shouts echo from the shower, without seeing an old gym sock dusty in a corner, or a tennis shoe collapsed on a bench with its tongue hanging out, even without lights, he could tell. His nose told him. In winter, the locker room reeked of muscle-rubbing liniment.

Jack plunked his gym bag down on one of the cold benches and began to change for the game. It was Friday afternoon, after school. Some of the boys from the other teams were a few lockers away getting dressed. They were laughing and chatting among themselves. Then Fred came in.

"Gee, Fred, am I glad to see *you*. I was beginning to think I would have to take on their whole team by myself."

"The others will be along in a minute. Say, you should have heard what I heard," said Fred, in a way that demanded the secret be dragged out of him.

"What'd you hear?"

"Oh, just a little tidbit that I picked up," said Fred, with a nonchalant shake of his head.

"Well, come on, tell me."

Fred held his arms out and spun around like a helicopter. He had snagged Jack's curiosity and wasn't ready to let him off the hook. Curious as he was, Jack still enjoyed this game of fishing – up to a point.

"Come on, Fred. Don't put me on or I'll let you have it!" Jack twisted his towel up and held it like he would snap Fred with it.

"You snap that towel at me, and I'll *never* tell you," said Fred, holding up his arms to protect himself. Jack stopped threatening Fred with his towel. Then, choosing his words carefully, Fred said:

"You remember after the Valentines party you told me that Jennifer had acted funny?"

"Yeah." Jack knew he'd never forget that day.

"Well, I think I know why she looked like she was crying." Now that he'd rebaited his hook, it looked like Fred might try to keep Jack dangling there awhile. Jack was just as determined to keep Fred talking.

"Fred, if you're making this up or just fooling, I'll tie your socks up in knots."

"I'm not fooling. This is real inside dope, so help me." Fred crossed his heart and took an oath on it.

127

"Okay, where'd you get your information? Who told you?"

"Fats."

"Fatima Swarts?" If Fatima had told Fred something, that would make it almost gospel truth, because she was one of Jennifer's closest friends. She was also the chief source of information in Ms. Rivera's class. She practically ran a news service. She was a girl that fellows could talk to, almost as easily as to their own sisters – maybe easier. "Tell me. What did Fats tell you?"

"First, I asked her to find out if Jennifer was mad at you again."

"And?"

"'Fats' found out that she's not. But that's not what's bothering Jennifer, anyway. It was about the valentine you gave her."

"For Pete's sake," frowned Jack. "I thought she'd like it. Heck, along with that joke valentine I gave you, and the monster ones I gave to Billy and Artie, it was one of the best cards I bought."

"I guess that's just it," said Fred, a bit mystified himself.

"What do you mean?"

"After you gave Jennifer such a fancy card, she was unhappy because she felt she hadn't given you one nearly as good."

Jack clapped his hand on his head and gave a sigh of relief.

"Oh, I thought I'd goofed again." When halfway near to understanding girls, a humdinger like this would happen which would almost persuade him on a career in the Foreign Legion. Just then, the rest of his teammates paraded into the locker room. Billy Suggs was in the lead, followed by Artie, Rodney, Donald, and Billy's cousin, Tubby Suggs.

"Everybody stand up and cheer! Ms. Rivera's team is here!" sang Billy, holding up a brown sack triumphantly in front of him.

"I thought you guys were *never* going to get here," said Jack. "Aren't we even going to warm up before the game?"

"Jack, you worry too much," said Billy. "No taboo things happened to you this week, did they?"

"Don't worry. I didn't break any mirrors, if that's what you mean," said Jack.

"Okay, good. That should clinch it then."

Fred got a twinkle in his eye and called out:

"You going to play on our team, Tubby? All you have to do is stand under the basket and nobody could get near it," he laughed.

"No. 'Tub's' going to take care of our lucky charms. Since he's not in our class, he can't play on our team," said Billy.

"Hey, fellas, look. See what I have?" Rodney held up a pair of bright new gym shoes. It was his annoying habit to try to sell himself through displaying his possessions.

"What about them?" said Billy. "Did you think we'd never seen a pair of gym shoes before?"

"I'll have you know, these are authentic official champion speedster shoes. See, they've even got the name of an All-Star champion on them."

"That's nothing," said Fred. "My shoes have *my* name on them. I don't go around hooking other guy's shoes like you do, Rodney."

Rodney snorted, but the other boys laughed.

Then everyone noticed that Artie was wildly rummaging through his locker.

"What's the matter, Artie?" asked Billy.

"I are got troubles, fellas," said Artie, holding his dimpled chin in one hand and scratching his head with the other.

"What are you looking for?"

"I looked everywhere and can't find my gym trunks nowhere. What are I going to do?"

"Let's see. There isn't time enough for you to run home and get them before the game, and you can't go out on the floor and play without them, that's for sure. We've got to find you another pair somewhere and quick. But where?"

The boys racked their brains over where to find gym shorts for Artie. Finally, Tubby Suggs came up with the solution. He went to his locker, opened his combination lock, and brought out *his* trunks.

"I'll lend you mine, Artie. They're a little big, but you can tighten up the belt."

Artie held Tubby's trunks and felt like he was staring down into a barrel. When he gamely climbed into them, the boys heaved a sigh of relief. That problem was solved.

"See? What'd I tell you? Now will you believe me when I tell you that luck is on our side?" Billy patted the bag with the lucky charms.

That minute, someone at the locker room door called, "Hey, aren't you ready yet? It's time for the game."

The boys walked into the barn-sized gym. Its floor was shiny as cellophane. Except for a few friends and classmates, the bleachers were empty.

"What positions are we going to play? Have we decided that yet?" asked Jack.

"Why do you always bring up such trivial matters? I've got to get these good luck charms properly set up for Tubby to watch over. You can figure out positions if you want to," called Billy, as he and Donald hustled over to the center bleachers, with Tubby lumbering behind them. Jack turned and had a huddle with Rodney, Artie, and Fred.

"Fred," said Jack, "how about you playing center? Artie and Rodney, you play guard, and Billy and I will play forward, okay?"

"But my speedster basketball shoes are officially for the center."

"We've already decided that Fred will start as center, Rodney. You can sub for him, then. And Don will start as guard. There's the whistle. Let's get out on the court."

The boys from Ms. Rivera's class had on green jerseys. The other team wore red.

Jack, waiting for the game to begin, felt like his insides were moving twice as fast as his outsides.

The referee tossed the ball in the air for the jump at center. The game was on. Fred tipped the ball to Artie. Artie went to catch the ball, then mysteriously dropped his hands to his sides. The ball bounced off his head and was taken by an opponent in for any easy layup shot. Two points.

"Green, take it out," said the referee, handing the ball to Artie. Artie made a one-handed toss to Donald, who then dribbled it down court. He fed it into Billy, who cut under the basket and tried the layup.

"Abracadabra!" yelled Billy.

The ball rolled around the rim three times and then off. The other team took the rebound and sailed the ball down the court to one of their players who was taking a fast break. Artie was under the basket, ready to block the shot. Suddenly and mysteriously, he dropped his hands again. The red player shot and scored another basket.

The first quarter ended with the score: 6 to 0.

"Artie, what are you doing out there?" asked Fred. Every time you have a chance to do some good, you're dropping your hands. How come?"

"It are either that, or drop my pants. Tubby's trunks won't stay up. Every time I raise my arms, my trunks slide down."

"Quick, run down to the locker room, and get Rodney to swap trunks with you."

The next two quarters were about as bad as the first. Billy stopped calling "abracadabra" to stop the other team. Since it wasn't bringing them good luck, he thought, maybe it would bring the other team bad luck. The red team kept scoring.

The boys met before the last quarter. Whatever they were doing, it wasn't working. Artie and Rodney switched trunks and returned to the gym floor. The score was 18 to 4.

"Now I'm really mad," said Billy. "Tubby, give 'em the old evil eye treatment."

Tubby stared daggers at the other team to put the hex on them. Billy reached down and picked up the sack with his most powerful lucky charms. Jack, Fred, and Rodney were standing by to see what Billy was going to do next, when it happened. Billy reached into the sack for the lucky jade stone. As he brought out his hand, the lucky horseshoe flipped out, bounced off Billy's foot, and landed on Arties big toe. They both let out a yelp and hopped around on one foot like grasshoppers on hot concrete.

After the boys had stopped hop-scotching around the gym floor, and the other boys had stopped laughing, Fred said:

"Isn't it time we made some plans and stopped mussing around with all this mumbo-jumbo?" But it turned out to be too late. For just then, the whistle blew and the last quarter of the game began. Artie and Billy limped back out on the court.

The end of the game was so much of a calamity, that it is better forgotten. With one foot aching, Billie and Artie staggered through the rest of the game. A few points were all that kept Ms. Rivera's team from being skunked completely.

After the game, the bedraggled team hobbled back to the locker room. They sat for a long time in silence.

"I can't understand it," said Billy finally, shaking his head. "I just can't understand it." He sat down on the bench and rubbed his sore foot. "How could we possibly lose? What happened? Did they have better lucky charms than we did?"

"I think maybe we should have practiced before the game like they did," said Fred.

At these words, Billy sprang angrily to his feet.

"Why? Didn't you think the lucky charms would work?" said Billy. His eyes glowed with fire.

"Well, I kind of doubted it," said Fred.

"That's it!" said Billy, pointing a finger at Fred. "Since you didn't believe in our lucky charms, you made us lose."

"What are you talking about? I made more points than you did," said Fred, bristling back at Billy.

There was a little pushing and shoving between Billy and Fred, and then Billy left in a huff.

On his way home, Jack thought over the whole basketball game. If they had won, the lucky charms would have gotten the credit. But since they lost, Billy blamed Fred. Jack couldn't help wondering who was right. Maybe by trusting more in the lucky charms they would have won. Why else were some things supposed to be good luck and others bad luck? It seemed reasonable, but Jack wasn't sure.

## CHAPTER XXII

# At the Monster Movie

Weeks passed by almost unnoticed. It was a Saturday morning in March. The first day of spring was still a few days away. After a dozen weeks of winter, Jack was tired of the snow and cold. Now, sitting at the breakfast table staring out the window, he watched the icicles on the garage roof dripping little craters in the snow while he dreamed of spring.

"Pass the corn flakes, puh-leez," said Nancy, holding out her hand. When Nancy spoke politely she often sounded more curt than courteous. She was never at her best in the morning. Her idea of a pleasant breakfast did not include brothers at the table.

"What the heck's wrong with this box. Somebody cut the back out of it," said Jack, as he reached for the cornflakes.

Peedie beamed his big toothless grin. "There was a Beatles cut-out on the back," he said.

Nancy looked cross. "I'm telling Mom. M-ah-m!"

Mrs. Holiday came running on the double. She was sure something terrible had happened like the ceiling falling in, or worse.

"Yes, Nancy. What is it?"

"Mom, Peedie cut the back out of the corn flakes box before it was empty," tattled Nancy.

"Oh, Peedie. You know what I told you about that," said Mrs. Holiday.

"That's not all, Mom," grumbled Nancy. "I spoke for that cutout first."

All Mrs. Holiday could do was sigh and wonder to herself if it was going to be another one of 'those days.' To her, Saturday was a day of mixed blessings. From experience, she knew that if Nancy, Jack, and Peedie had something to keep them busy, there would be peace. Otherwise, even the United Nations would be helpless to prevent the squabbles or settle them.

"What have you got planned for today?" asked Mrs. Holiday. She looked from one munching face to the next for an answer.

Finally, Nancy said, "Well, if the roller rink is open, I'd like to go skating. Especially if I can get one of my friends to go with me."

"Okay, Nancy. You can tidy up your room, and I'll give you money enough to go skating," said Mrs. Holiday. "And that goes for Peedie and you too, Jack. Clean up your rooms and take the papers out, and you can earn some money to do something today. Have you got any ideas?"

"Well, I'd like to go to the show," said Jack.

"Me, too!" said Peedie.

"Aw, I knew there'd be a catch to it," grumbled Jack.

"Now, Jack," said Mother. "Taking care of the wastepaper baskets and cleaning up your own room isn't asking a whole lot of you."

It's not that. It's just that,…does Peedie have to do everything I do?"

"No. But certainly it's not going to hurt you to sit in the same movie theater with him."

"Okay, but don't blame me if he has bad dreams. It's a scary movie. Last time he went with me, he couldn't look at the picture."

"I could so!" said Peedie, thrusting up his snub nose at Jack.

"Yeah. Why'd you hide under the seat then?"

"I wasn't hiding. I dropped my popcorn."

"Oh, sure."

"Wanna bet?"

"Boys, boys. It doesn't matter. Get busy on your jobs or you won't have time to finish them before the show."

The children went up to their rooms to begin project 'cleanup'. Digging into the pyramids of stuff that had piled up and clogged the closet, made the place look more like a warehouse than a bedroom. First, everything that had been hidden away was brought out. This made it seem like Jack and Peedie were magicians, making things appear out of thin air. Next began the archeological stage. Peedie, like a digger into the past, began unearthing "buried" treasure.

"Peedie, are you going to help or just play around?" asked Jack.

"I *am* helping. I'm sorting out things."

"Oh, sure. It's taken all this time to sort out two toy cars."

"I'm looking for one of the wheels."

"How come when we've got a ton of stuff to put away, you spend all your time looking for one dinky wheel?"

"You ever try to drive on three wheels?"

At that minute, Mrs. Holiday decided to look in and see how the project was going. When she saw the room piled nearly to the ceiling, she almost fainted. All the clutter had been dragged out and stacked on the beds, till they looked like a couple of mountains.

"Oh Jack, it looks worse than when you started," said Mrs. Holiday, pitching in to give them a hand. Mrs. Holiday began wrestling with one of the piles and dumping some of the scattered parts into the waste basket.

"Mom, why'd you throw that away? That's a part to our secret agent set. Let us do the sorting. You don't know which things are good."

"I guess I don't," Mrs. Holiday said with a sigh. "It all looks like junk to me. All I know is, you'd better hurry. You only have an hour before the matinee begins."

"Don't worry. We'll get it done. Come on Peedie, help, so we can get done in time for the show."

Peedie and Jack went back to their cleanup task with new energy. Soon, their bedroom was back to its original order – or disorder. Everything had been crammed back into place. Soon, the boys dashed off to the movie theater.

In no time, Jack and his little brother were squeezed into line with the rest of the chattering crowd waiting for the ticket seller to open up the box office. The smell of popcorn wafted through the lobby. When it came Jack's turn to buy tickets, he stooped slightly at the ticket window. He knew that soon he wouldn't be able to get in for half-price. At the door, a sleepy-eyed attendant yawned, took their tickets, and tore them in half. Peedie insisted on handing over his own ticket. They walked down the aisle and sat down before the giant movie screen. Peedie's eyes flashed with excitement, while Jack acted bigger by staying calm. The theater was stirring with lively faces that bobbed around like playful mice in a cage. Then the theater dimmed and the screen was ablaze with light. The crowd cheered as the movie started.

It was at that moment – the moment before all the movie titles had been shown and the actual story begun – that Jack's attention was drawn away from the screen and toward the movement of three late-comers to the theater. Jack's heart jumped. He couldn't understand why, at first, but his instinct, even in that darkened theater, was lightning quick. There was something about their jackets and their swaggers that labeled them, as surely as if the three boys had been in a spotlight.

Halfway down the aisle, the boy in front turned and looked down the rows for seats, as the flickering light from the movie screen was reflected off of his vicious, piggy face. There was no doubt about it. It was Casper, the bully who called himself Jasper.

Jasper spat on the carpet. And then with a fling of his head, led his two rat-like followers into a row where they plunked themselves noisily down into seats.

Peedie's attention, all this while, was glued to the screen. It was a good thing, thought Jack, that Peedie didn't know anything about these bullies. Jack felt very protective over his little brother at that moment.

The film story ground on to its smashing finish. At the end of the show, Jack and Peedie followed the tide of boisterous children as the crowd emptied out of the movie into the glare of daylight once more. Jack looked around, but saw nothing more of Jasper and his creepy sidekicks. Soon, Peedie and Jack had walked back home. It was time for them to sit down for supper.

"Mmm! Something smells good. What are we having for supper?" Jack asked his mother.

"Spaghetti. You and Peedie go get washed up," said Mrs. Holiday, who was stirring the sauce. Jack sniffed the aroma as Peedie sneaked a look at the supper cooking.

The pan of sauce was bubbling on the burner.

When Jack had finished washing and Peedie was half-washed, they returned to the kitchen. Mr. Holiday was seated at the table already, and Nancy was where she could sit by him. Nancy liked to sit next to Mom and Dad. The kitchen was large and light and was often used instead of the dining room for most ordinary meals. The dining room was saved mostly for company. The table was set. And as soon as the boys sat down, Mother served each one in turn.

Everyone in the family had their own way of eating spaghetti. Mr. Holiday's method was to twirl his spaghetti on his fork with the aid of a large spoon. Mrs. Holiday would work a cluster onto the tip of her fork before lifting it from the plate. Jack ate his spaghetti whichever way he could, juggling as he went along. Nancy leaned over her dish and, in that way, cut the distance between pickup and delivery. But Peedie's method was, above all, the most unique. His was as logical and workable as the rest – although Mrs. Holiday often frowned on it.

Peedie's way was to seize a strand of spaghetti and, as if whistling backwards, slurp it in. It looked something like an electric cord being reeled back into a vacuum cleaner. The thought of how little birds feed did not make Peedie's method very appetizing to watch.

When she could no longer stand the sight or slurp of it, Mrs. Holiday would sometimes cut up Peedie's spaghetti to spoon-size.

"I'll bet Peedie's the only one who can eat spaghetti without opening his jaw," laughed Jack. "All he has to do is suck it in through his missing baby teeth."

"Jack, remember what I told you about teasing," said Mrs. Holiday.

Then to change the subject, Mr. Holiday said, "How was the movie, boys?" Father should have known better than to ask that question, especially at the dinner table. But before he could correct his mistake, and before Jack even had a chance to speak, Peedie's face lit up under a smear of spaghetti sauce, and he was off.

"Oh, Dad. It was neat! There was this scraggly-haired scientist who talked funny and wanted to do something great for the world. So he, and this hunched-over guy who grunted funny, went to graveyards and stuff. Then they have this real neat laboratory, see? It's in this cobwebby old castle on a mountain outside of town. And it's filled with bottles and electrical junk. Then there's this nutty lady who keeps worrying that something terrible's going to happen. You know the kind. She's daffy over this guy with muscles, who's always sunning himself. Well, she kept worrying, and he kept telling her not to – that nothing would happen – and how the doctor's a great scientist and all. Then there's this corny part. *Yecch*! He has to kiss her to keep her from worrying. Anyhow, it got better after that."

Peedie hadn't eaten a bite since he'd galloped on about the movie. "Your spaghetti is getting cold, Peedie. Hadn't you better finish your supper first, and tell us your story later?" said Mrs. Holiday.

"Wait, Mom," said Peedie. "There's only a little more – the neat part. After that, it was night. And it rained, and thundered, and big lightning bolts flashed in the sky. The scientist with the scraggly-hair, who used to have pet rabbits and stuff, gets this real crazy look on his face. And his helper leaps around the room and pulls on all these electric switches. And these big sparks go *crackly, zap, bam*! And then the scientist is really nutty and he hollers out: 'Ach Himmel. I haff discuffert efferlastingk lieff!' And the hunched-over guy cackles real neat, too.

Oh, and I almost forgot. That fraidy-cat dame was there, too – tied up, screaming, and worrying, and going on something awful. They'd caught her snooping in the castle. You know how nosy girls are. Well, the other guy with the neat muscles comes looking for her at the castle and hears her scream. So he comes to the castle and beats down this big thick door with his fists. When he sees all the sparks and stuff, he goes wild and yells out something like people shouldn't mess around with nature. Then he tears into all the scientist's stuff and knocks it over – *kerblammity bash*! And everything starts exploding – *pckoosh! pckoosh*! Then the neat guy grabs the nutty dame and runs out. The place is all on fire - stuff falling down, and everything. And then the whole castle goes *BLAMMO*, and blows up!"

Everybody breathed a sigh of relief when Peedie had finished telling about the movie.

That night, Jack had a dream about the movie. In his dream, he was the hero with the big muscles. Jennifer was the beautiful girl saved from the mad doctor's laboratory. And the big old castle that blew up and fell down in the movie, in Jack's dream, blew up and fell down on a mad scientist with a piggy face - just like Jasper's.

## CHAPTER XXIII

# A Distant Dream Delayed

There was nothing Jack liked more than a vacation. Whole dream worlds were drummed up in wait for those lordly days away from school. As the time approached, the clock hands seemed to crawl along and schoolwork got flat and tedious. Jack would begin to tire of facts such as Balboa being first to see the Pacific. He longed to see something more exciting than the school blackboard.

Finally, the day came and Jack stuffed his school books into his desk for Easter recess. He could hardly wait to get home, change his clothes, and get outdoors and celebrate. Even though it would be a short vacation and Jack had made no plans, he intended to make the most of each day. Just to be free to talk all he wanted and not be shushed up, free to run outside as fast as he wanted and not have the time up as quick as in gym, just to be outdoors with spring in the air, was worth everything. On his way home, Jack met Benjie.

"Hi, Benjie."

"Oh, hi Jack," beamed Benjie, his eyes beginning to shine. Benjie looked up to Jack with almost hero worship. Partly, because Jack was two grades ahead of Benjie in school. They walked along without saying much at first, just taking in the scenery.

"When are we going to go scare the girls again?" asked Benjie.

"You mean like last summer?"

"Yeah!"

"Well…"

Benjie's eyes lost a little of their luster. "Then it's true what Rodney told me. I didn't believe Rodney was telling me right."

"Why, what did he tell you?"

Benjie just continued to walk along side of Jack with his hands deep in his pockets. His mind searching for words to give voice to his troubled thoughts.

"If that Rodney's making up any big story about me, I want to hear it," said Jack. "So, out with it. What'd he say?"

"He says you've got a girlfriend named Jennifer."

Jack could see that his stock as a hero was bound to plummet with his young friend, unless he could redeem himself. It was crushing for Benjie to find out that his hero liked girls.

"You don't believe everything you hear, do you? Rodney's probably just saying that because girls don't like him much. Don't pay any attention to him."

"Then how come you haven't been around much?" said Benjie, still wanting desperately to believe the best of Jack.

"Well, we've had all these games after school. And then, you know, what with school and winter and all, I've been indoors a lot. Say, do you ever see anything more of the old go-cart we made last summer?"

"Oh gee, no. That was cool, too!" said Benjie, rubbing his hands under his chin. His eyes were glowing once more. Mention of the go-cart made him forget all about the girlfriend business.

"Remember how Rodney hit the bump on the sidewalk and crashed right through M. Yeager's hedge, and ended up smack over his lawn sprinkler?"

Benjie giggled, shaking all over.

The memory of Rodney like a statue in a fountain in the center of Mr. Yeager's lawn sprinkler with water seeming to squirt out of his ears and everywhere, made the boys practically do handsprings. After they'd laughed till they were weak, Benjie said, "Do you think Mary Jane would let us use the wheels again?"

"No, I don't think Mary Jane'd go much for the idea. Remember, she got spanked for letting us take those wheels off the family buggy," said Jack.

"Oh yeah. Remember how we almost thought Mary Jane's baby sister, Babsy, had swallowed my caterpillar, but it only had fallen off the stick into the buggy?"

"What would we have done if Babsy really had eaten the caterpillar?"

"I dunno. Guess she would have had butterflies in her stomach."

Another round of laughter followed. This time, they nearly split their sides. Finally, they stood in front of the sidewalk leading up to Jack's house. For a minute, after they had recovered from their laughing, they watched a robin hop along on the lawn, tilt its head to listen, then peck at the ground and hop along some more.

"What are you going to do during vacation?" asked Benjie.

"I don't know. I haven't made up my mind yet," said Jack.

"Why can't we build another go-cart?" suggested Benjie.

"Know where we can get some wheels?" asked Jack.

"No."

"That's why."

Benjie toyed with a stone with his foot. "Isn't there something else we could build?"

"Um, I *do* have one idea I've been thinking about."

"What's that?" said Benjie, with an eager new glimmer in his eye.

"Well, I've just been thinking about it to myself, so far. I haven't told anybody about it yet."

"Come on, Jack. Tell me. I helped you good with the go-cart didn't I?"

"Yeah, but this is something bigger, *much* bigger."

Jack had so sharpened his curiosity now that Benjie was practically drooling to find out.

"Please, Jack. Tell me."

"Okay, but don't talk it around. You promise?"

"I promise."

"Swear to it? I wouldn't want certain guys to hear about it."

"I swear," said Benjie, doing a flurry of heart crossings and hand signals. "Tell me, Jack."

"Not a word about it to anyone, but I've been thinking of building a clubhouse."

"A clubhouse? Where?" Benjie lit up like a Christmas tree.

"Shush. Not so loud. Remember, you can't tell who might be listening."

"Where would we build it?" whispered Benjie.

"In my backyard. I haven't worked out all the details, mind you. I'm just making plans for it now."

Benjie rushed home to change his clothes. Jack ambled up the walk to his house. The minute he entered, Jack heard his name called. The house seemed to be alive with get–readiness. Jack sensed it immediately.

"Jack, is that you?"

"Yeah, Mom."

"Come on up and get ready. We're driving to Cleveland."

Jack bounded up the stairs. Mrs. Holiday had a suitcase on the bed and was folding clothes into it. Dad's new suit and several of Mom's dresses were hanging in a garment bag on the closet door. Mrs. Holiday was already dressed up to go visiting.

"Cleveland?" Jack asked.

"Yes, to visit Aunt Lulu and Uncle Ollie. Don't' you remember, I mentioned it last week?" said Mrs. Holiday.

"Oh yeah," moaned Jack. He wondered to himself why he always forgot things like that.

The rest of their preparations looked like an old-time movie. They darted in, they darted out. Grabbing, stacking, packing. Squeezing luggage to latch it. Mother in a dither, pushing Peedie, prodding Nancy. Jack tugging, twisting, and turning luggage in the car trunk to get the lid down. At last, the house was locked up, the Holiday family car was backed out of the driveway, and they were on their way to Cleveland, three-hundred miles away.

Jack looked out the car window as the countryside rushed by. The trees were still stark and lifeless as sticks, but there nubbled branches gave hints of budding. The sun was orange off the tree limbs. The grass, matted by winter, was greening. And crocuses gave touches of color in places. The sky was a bright blue with little cotton puffs of clouds. The landscape trembled with freshness and renewal.

"We almost there?" asked Peedie, who was sitting so far forward on the backseat that his chin rested on the back of the front seat.

"Peedie, we're hardly out of town yet," said Mr. Holiday.

"Yeah, Peedie," Jack kidded. "We've only got about two-hundred ninety-nine more miles to go."

Peedie had no idea of distance. He began to get fidgety the minute the car left the driveway, if not before.

"Did you read in the newspaper what happened at the movie theater, Dorothy?" Mr. Holiday asked Mrs. Holiday.

"You mean about several cartons of candy bars being stolen from the refreshment counter? Isn't that terrible? According to the paper, they had been left on the counter and weren't being watched. Why do you think they were so careless as to leave those out like that?"

"Well, for one thing, the movie had already let out, so they didn't think anyone was around. They're really hoping that it wasn't very young children who took them, though."

"Why is that?" asked Mrs. Holiday.

"Well, to top it all off, I've since heard that it wasn't exactly candy bars after all. It was mixed up with an order for a drugstore, and received by the theater by mistake.

That's why it was left out on the counter. It was being sent back to the supply company."

"Why? What was wrong with the candy, Dad?" asked Jack, who had been listening in on the conversation. He remembered that he and Peedie had been to the movies on Saturday. At the same time, he had seen Jasper and his gang there.

"Nothing was wrong with it, Jack, used in the right way. Only thing, is it wasn't really candy. It was laxative!"

"What's a laxative?" asked Peedie.

"That's what Mom gives you when you can't go to the bathroom, Stoop," said Jack.

"So you see, Peedie, it wouldn't be much of a treat for anybody who doesn't read labels. In fact," laughed Mr. Holiday, "It would be more of a treat*ment*."

Up till then, Peedie, Nancy, and Jack had chattered excitedly or quarreled over little differences of opinion. Finally, as the miles rolled away under them, they became weary and silent, or fell asleep. When they reached Cleveland, it was dark. Aunt Lulu and Uncle Oliver came out to greet them. Peedie was carried in and put right to bed. Sleepy-eyed, Nancy and Jack dragged themselves to bed, too.

Jack didn't fall asleep as easily as Peedie, even after the long tiring ride. The excitement at being in a strange house and in a strange room kept him awake. While he lay in bed, Jack thought about the theft at the movie theater. He didn't know whether Jasper and his creepy sidekicks had done it, but he was convinced of one thing – they were crummy enough to have done it.

Then it dawned on Jack that he hadn't phoned Benjie to tell him he would be away. Poor Benjie, he thought. He'll come to my house looking for me to build a clubhouse and I'll be gone. For the rest of the night, Jack dreamt of how great it would be to build and have a clubhouse.

## CHAPTER XXIV

# A Visit to Cleveland

In the morning, when Jack awoke, he was startled to find himself in a strange bed and in a strange room. He rubbed and blinked his eyes and looked again. Then he remembered – he was at his Aunt Lulu's house. Snuggled up in the covers beside him, slumbering like the angel he wasn't, was Peedie. On mornings when there was no school, Peedie was usually the first one up. This morning, he was still sound asleep. The three-hundred-mile ride to Cleveland had exhausted him. He had tried to stay awake the whole trip – no matter what – but he finally had to give in to sleep.

Jack looked first at the wallpaper. Then he studied the pictures on the walls. Last of all, he studied the furniture. Strange things in new places always brought out the explorer in him. Sun streaming in through the window drew his attention outside. He got out of bed and peered out at Aunt Lulu's backyard. Her small lawn was bordered by a dark green hedge. In the center of it was a white trellis, a birdbath, and two ornamental pink flamingoes.

Jack got up, dressed, and went downstairs. He was eager to see Uncle Ollie, and maybe get him to tell a story. When he came down the stairs he heard voices coming from the kitchen. Jack sauntered in. Mrs. Holiday was sitting at the breakfast table sipping a cup of coffee. Across from her was Mr. Holiday who was reading the morning newspaper. Nancy had a seat between them. She was as bright as a pixie, probably from the extra attention she was getting from Aunt Lulu.

"Good morning, Jack," said Mrs. Holiday. "Is Peedie up?"

"Morning, Mom. No. He's still sound asleep."

Aunt Lulu turned and smiled at Jack. She had an apron tied around her waist and was standing at the kitchen range frying sausages. Jack could hear them sizzle and crackle in the pan.

"Good morning, Jack," she drawled. "My, how you've grown. Come give your Auntie a big hug."

Jack went over and got squeezed like a wrestler in an arm-lock. He was thankful that his Aunt wasn't wearing any of her prickly stabbing brooches.

Aunt Lulu served Jack his breakfast.

"Where's Uncle Ollie?" asked Jack.

"Uh, he's …downtown, dear. Nancy, are you ready for more pancakes?" Nancy grinned, licked her lips, and held up her plate.

Jack scarfed down his breakfast, then left the table to go exploring. Aunt Lulu's house seemed as tidy as a department store. The furniture was shiny and spotless. The most noticeable thing about Aunt Lulu's living room, besides the frilly lace curtains, were the embroidered cloth doilies. They were draped all over everything like so many pancakes. There were doilies under vases, and doilies on coffee tables, and doilies on the arms and backs of chairs and couches. Jack sat down. The doily on the chair back slipped down, and the one on the arm rest slid off onto the floor. Jack picked them up and smoothed and straightened them, and then decided he'd better not sit down. He had a feeling that if anything got moved, it would most certainly be noticed. Next, Jack looked around the room for something to do. The magazines were all ladies' magazines. Even the television set looked like it was for grown-ups only. Since Aunt Lulu didn't have any children, he couldn't find anything to do.

Once again, a long-awaited vacation fell short of his dreams. Jack and Peedie spent the day wandering listlessly about, showing Aunt Lulu how "grown-up" they were. Most of the time, they kept their hands in their pockets so they wouldn't tip over anything breakable, like the knick-knacks that Aunt Lulu had all over the house. Most of them were glass angels or cupids. It seemed to Jack that the fragile figurines had silly sly looks on their puffy faces and would fall over and break just to get a guy in trouble. Jack was sure that if one did fall over, it would end up pointing a finger at him.

Saturday crawled on to bedtime while the grownups visited. The next morning was Easter.

At the break of morning, even before the birds were awake, Peedie was up. First thing he did was search for his Easter basket. He looked behind the couch and under the chairs. He looked in every hiding place he could think of, but he didn't find any baskets.

"Mom," called Peedie, waking up his mother, "didn't the Easter Bunny come? Or doesn't he come to Aunt Lulu's?"

"Oh," answered Mrs. Holiday, yawning, "you'll find baskets on the kitchen table."

"Jeepers," said Peedie, "even the Easter Bunny doesn't do things right for kids at Aunt Lulu's house."

The children nibbled away at their candy before going to church. Peedie, of course, got a chocolate spot on his clean shirt, first thing. Mother, sighing deeply, scrubbed at it with a wet cloth.

"Try to keep your clothes from getting wrinkled," she said.

The rest of Easter Sunday, including Sunday dinner, Jack spent trying to keep his good clothes good by being uncomfortable in them. It seemed to Jack that it was impossible to keep clothes from getting wrinkly, since people just naturally bend in places.

Up till now, Peedie, Jack, and Nancy had only seen Uncle Oliver for a few minutes. He seemed to spend an awful lot of time downtown. Jack couldn't blame him. There was no chair a fellow could sit comfortably on, especially when doilies kept slipping around. And almost everywhere, you were stared at by a lot of little knick-knack statues. Besides, Jack had overheard Mother say that if Uncle Ollie wanted to read his newspaper, he couldn't sit in the living room. Jack wondered how his Uncle could keep his sense of humor through it all. On this night, to the children's delight, Uncle Oliver came home before they were asleep.

"Oh, tell us a story, Uncle Ollie," they begged, jumping up and down.

"I think the dears are too tired for a story tonight, Oliver."

"No, we're not, Aunt Lulu, no we're not." Finally, since it wasn't a school night, they got their wish. And Uncle Oliver followed them up to bed.

Uncle Oliver brought a book off the shelf and thumbed through some pages.

"How would you like me to read you the story of "Kazim, the Goatboy," said Uncle Oliver.

"Did he have horns, Uncle Ollie?"

"No, Peedie, Kazim wasn't a goat any more than a cowboy is a cow," laughed Uncle Oliver.

"For Pete's sake, Peedie, if you're going to ask a lot of goofy questions, we'll never get to hear the story. Go ahead and read to us, Uncle Ollie."

Peedie made a face at Jack. And Jack made one back.

Uncle Oliver sat down on the edge of the bed, adjusted the book for the best light, cleared his throat, then began:

### 'KAZIM THE GOATBOY'

*"In days long gone, there lived two brothers - one named Abiss and the other Kazim. Their father, a carpenter by trade, liked the older son, Abiss, but he adored his younger son, Kazim. Even though Abiss, the eldest son, would inherit his father's lands, he was troubled by all the attention given to his younger brother. Every time the father smiled at Kazim, the envy of Abiss increased until hatred of his younger brother began to work at him like a worm in an apple.*

*It was in these days that the land was afflicted with a dry spell that so parched the Earth that there was not a blade of grass to feed the family's herd of goats. As the youngest son, it was Kazim's duty to tend the herd. So, one day, his father put the shepherd's staff in his hand and offered up a prayer for him. And his mother placed a goat skin of precious sweet water over his shoulder and kissed him. And they bid him take the goats to the high ground, where they might find some grass on which to graze.*

*'Take care that nothing happens to the ram' said the father - for he prized one of the goats over all the others, as it was indeed an animal of exceeding value.*

*Kazim promised to guard it with his life.*

*When Kazim was gone, his mother wept and sorrowed greatly for his safety. And his father comforted her, and fought back the tears that streaked his own wrinkled cheek. Only one person had dry eyes – that was Abiss, the elder son.*

*Kazim had never been far from home. It was dusk when he reached the cliffs whose rocks jutted out on both sides like teeth. The land was desolate and without inhabitants. Kazim walked along the valley until it became night. When the cold moist dew of night descended, he bedded down with the goats to wait for morning. During the first night, he experienced great terrors. Rocks shrouded in darkness seemed to come alive. Thorny branches waved to beckon like taloned claws. The strange landscape seemed filled with evil spirits.*

*Twenty days under the broiling sun, and twenty nights under the diamond stars, Kazim herded the goats. And he was lonely.*

*In his solitude, he became acquainted with the rocks and shrubs and the mysteries of the night.*

*At home, his mother wrung her hands and wailed: 'Oh what will become of him? What will become of my son?'*

*To this, her older son answered: 'Everything that is to be must be, and no man knows what will befall him.'*

*In those twenty days and twenty nights, Kazim's father and mother ceased not to worry, and he was more in their minds than ever before. The favor that Abiss hoped to gain in his younger brother's absence did not come. Even away, Kazim's claim to his father's affections grew till the thought of his returning became intolerable to Abiss. Abiss knew if he could steal the prized ram away from Kazim, it would bring disgrace down upon his brother's head.*

*That night when the shadows were deepest, Abiss stole away from home. He marched overland in the direction of the high ground and jutting tooth-like rock cliffs. The bleating of the goats led him to the very spot where his younger brother was encamped.*

*When he had crept to within a few feet of his sleeping brother, he hid in a bush and called out through cupped hands to disguise his voice: 'Ka---zim. Ka---zim!'*

*The voice startled Kazim out of his sleep. Taking his staff, he rose to his feet and stared into the darkness. The mysterious voice seemed to come from a patch of bushes.*

*'Who is calling me?' stammered Kazim, wondering greatly at hearing a bush talk.*

*'Ka---zim, flee from here at once. Leave the goats and go!' Abiss wanted to get rid of his brother, but he didn't want to lose the family's goats.*

*'Go, or I will get you. Whoo-oo!'*

*Now it came to pass, by way of his experience in the wilderness, that Kazim had grown in manhood.*

*Instead of running from his brother's attempt to scare him, Kazim decided to probe the mysterious bush with his staff. When he poked his staff into the bush, it landed on his brother's head. Here, he had found something of substance, not just a voice in a bush."*

"Which all goes to show that one should never beat around the bush – when one can beat *on* it."

Uncle Oliver clapped the book shut. His eyes twinkled over his red potato of a nose. "Get under your covers," he said.

"You know something, Uncle Oliver?"

"What's that, Peedie?"

"Jack tries to scare *me* sometimes."

"I do not," complained Jack.

"You do, too."

Uncle Oliver was standing with his hand on the wall light switch at the bedroom door. Suddenly he got a jolly look on his face and chuckled: "You know, Peedie, maybe Jack is just trying to get *your* goat. Good night, kids."

## CHAPTER XXV

# Starting the Treehouse

"Please, Dad?"

"It's no use teasing, Jack. You can't build a clubhouse in the yard."

"Even out back?"

"Not even out back. You know how Mr. Yeager next door complains. And then there's the zoning ordinance. I'm sorry. I'd like you to have a clubhouse, but it's just not possible."

Jack's argument was cut short as Mr. Holiday returned to his evening newspaper. Jack knew the newspaper signaled the end of the discussion – meeting adjourned. Even though his hopes were dashed, Jack couldn't put his dreams of a clubhouse out of his mind. Then he remembered with a thread of hope that Benjie might have asked *his* dad, too. Jack wanted to have the clubhouse at his place, but having it at Benjie's would be the next best thing.

As Jack walked down the street to Benjie's house his thoughts simmered in him like a low blue flame. A person can stand just so much disappointment before he begins to boil inside.

Jack's slow burn had begun by having to spend his vacation in Cleveland at Aunt Lulu's house. There was just not enough elbow room for him, hemmed in as he was by lace curtains, doilies, and dainty knick-knacks. It fried him, too, that he'd had to spend his days off from school dressed so namby-pamby good. Always having to act to suit grownups made Jack steam under his collar. Then there was the added friction of too much vacation time spent with his little brother and sister. One grievance had enflamed another. Not to be turned down on building a clubhouse was the final stick to the blaze.

Jack just couldn't make out why grownups didn't understand kids better. They'd all been kids once themselves.

When Jack left the house, he wouldn't have been upset if the back door had slammed off its hinges. Once outside, though, the mild weather soothed his temper some. Munching the cookie he'd snitched from the cookie jar, he looked around him as he walked along. The daffodils were out, the maple trees were sprouting, and the days were beginning to grow longer. Except for a few vacant lots, there were houses along both sides of Jack's street. Really it wasn't his street, but he called it his for he knew Elm Street as well as any kid on the block, and better than most grownups.

Jack's territory went from six houses up the street to eight houses down the street. Within these houses lied all his closest neighborhood pals, like Billy and

Benjie and Rodney. Jack liked his home and neighborhood, but he often dreamed about having a place of his own. In his dreams, it would become a wilderness place or a secret place – a fort, a shack, a cabin, a clubhouse, even sometimes a cave.

Boxes or pieces of wood would often suggest such places to his imagination. Jack's imagination was a much faster builder than he was. It could raise towers with secret doors faster than the blink of an eye. When it came to really doing the building, there were always several problems – like where to build, what tools and materials to use, and how to get it done. The last problem – how to get it done, was seldom reached. The problem of where and what to build with seemed impossible to solve.

When Jack reached Benjie's house, he had lost some of his anger, but he hadn't given up his idea of a clubhouse. Benjie met Jack at the door.

"Did you ask your dad about building one in your backyard?" asked Benjie.

Benjie's little sister, Ellen, was peeking out the door. "Build what?" she asked.

"None of your business, nosy. Come on, Jack. Let's go somewhere else so we won't be snooped on."

Ellen stuck out her tongue at them and Benjie razzed her back. Then they moved off down the street.

Jack hop-frogged over a fire hydrant. Benjie was all set to, but then decided at the last minute it was safer to walk.

"What'd your dad say about building a clubhouse?" asked Benjie.

Jack shook his head. "Any chance we could build it in *your* yard?" he asked.

Benjie shook his head. "My dad's worse than your dad about things like that. Besides, my little sister's a bigger snoop than yours, anyway. Guess we'll have to give up on the idea, huh, Jack?"

Jack kept scuffling along. His jaw was set, and his lips were closed tight. He was turning things over in his mind. He was wishing he lived on a farm or out in the woods, where it was possible to build things and nobody would care. Suddenly, Jack stopped and clapped his fist into his cupped hand.

"You got an idea?" asked Benjie.

"Sure! I should have thought of it before. I think I know where we could build a clubhouse."

"Where, Jack, where?"

"You ever been over by the Old Swinging Bridge?"

"No, I don't think so."

"Well, it's near Artie's house. There are lots of trees there and it's kind of wild. And the creek runs right by it. I'm going to go see Artie about it. Can you come with me? Or won't your folks let you?"

"I can come as long as I'm back about eight-thirty."

"Okay. Come on, let's go."

Jack and Benjie hurried down Elm Street over Academy then down Dobbins past the cemetery and the rickety house that kids called haunted. Soon they were on Creek Street. Jack just had to surprise Benjie with the neat hollow tree that Billy Suggs had shown him. Then they walked over the springy old swinging bridge. Benjie got a little green-looking crossing over the narrow bridge, but then most kids did, crossing it for the first time. Soon, they had climbed up the steep embankment to Artie's weird house and we're knocking at his saggy screen door. The flaky paint grated against Jack's knuckles as he knocked. From inside, they could hear some mumbling. And then the door opened. It was Artie's Dad.

"What'dya want?" he bellowed.

"Uh, can we talk to Artie?'

"Artie! Some kids here to see ya," he shouted.

Mr. Armstrong went back and sat down at a kitchen table covered with a red checkered oil cloth. Artie came into the kitchen. Jack could see him through the rusted-out patch in the screen.

"Are it for me?" said Artie.

"Just kids," growled Mr. Armstrong.

"Artie? It's me, Jack. Come on out. I've got something to talk over with you."

Outside, the boys walked over to the bank and sat on the rusty bumper of the junk automobile. Down below through the budding trees, they could see the creek. Its brown water swirled by, swelling with the spring runoff. Even from that height they could hear the swift rushing of the current.

"Who owns that land along the creek, Artie?"

Artie held his palms out and shrugged his shoulders. "It are mostly wild. And mostly it's used for dumping trash. One time I was down there when a tin can came flying over the bank and knocked me right in the head. See? I still got a scar from it." Benjie and Jack marveled at his thin, white scar.

"Gee, that's neat for playing pirates, Artie."

"Aw, it are nothing, really. Now tell me, you thought up something new?"

"As a matter of fact, yes. Benjie and I got an idea about building a clubhouse, but we haven't got any place to build it."

"Oh," said Artie. "I are always been thinking of building one of those, myself. Trouble is, the trees are so thick, there's no room around her neither."

"Let's have a look around, anyway," said Jack.

The boys edged carefully down the steep bank. Sometimes one of them would slip and grab hold of a small tree to stop himself from sliding all the way down. Once down, they pushed through the dense verdant undergrowth along the creek's edge, looking for a likely place to build.

"See how thick it are down here."

But Jack did not answer Artie. His attention was drawn up into the trees. An idea was beginning to flicker across his mind. "Since there's not much clear space to build on the ground," said Jack patting the bark of a v-shaped tree, "let's build up there. We'll build a tree house!"

The boys craned their necks looking up into the treetops. His eyes sparkling with hope, Benjie rubbed his hands under his chin, while Artie bit his lower lip in dreamy contemplation.

"Well, what do you think of the idea?" asked Jack.

"It are good enough with me," said Artie. "What now?"

"Let's climb up." Jack leaped for one of the lower branches and began pulling himself up. After he climbed up to the next height branch, Artie followed him into the tree. The bark of the trunk felt cobbly to their hands, but the tree's branches were smoother to grip. Jack and Artie perched in the branches like Indian scouts, and surveyed the scent. The view was so fascinating that they forgot about Benjie. Unable to jump high enough to reach the first limb, he had tried to shimmy up the tree trunk but had slid back.

"Hey, you guys. How about giving me a push up this thing?"

Jack and Artie looked down and laughed.

"Hold on, Benjie. We're coming down anyway. Artie, where could we get some wood to put across these limbs?" With his hands, Jack showed where he would put the wood.

"There are some old wood up in back of my house."

"Could we use some of it?" asked Jack.

"I think it are okay."

"Good. Let's go take a look at it."

Artie and Jack swung down to the ground, and Benjie slid down the short distance that he'd tried to shimmy up. The boys climbed up the steep lumpy side of the bank again. Behind Arties house was a pile of wood. The boards were gray and rough and weathered.

"Sure your Dad won't care if we use some of this wood?" said Jack, teetering on one of the planks.

"Naw, he won't care. He never builds nothing anyway. It are going to be tough carrying them down the hill, though."

"Oh, I don't think so," said Jack, looking over the side with his neck outstretched. "Let's do it the lumberjack way. You know how they slide logs down the side of a bank.

One after another, the boys grabbed hold of pieces of wood and slid or rolled them down the bank, laughing as they worked. Some of the pieces landed right at the foot of the tree they had picked. Others snagged on saplings or clods part way down. And one slid clear past the tree, and splashed into the creek. Of course, the boys hated to lose the piece, but the sight of it sailing down the creek with the current made them burst out laughing.

"I think that's enough for now," said Jack.

Slipping down the embankment, the boys collected the pieces that had got hung up on the way down and piled them all at the foot of their tree. They then stood looking up at where they hoped to build. Already in Jack's imagination, he could see a magnificent treehouse with all kinds of gadgets and secret stuff in it. Jack climbed eagerly back into the tree. He held himself in place by locking his legs around a branch.

"Okay, Artie. Hand me up that big plank near your foot." Jack called down.

Artie raised it over his head, Benjie giving him a hand as well as he could. The board began to sway back and forth, like a juggler's stick.

"I can't reach it, Artie. Push it up higher. Push!"

"I are. I are! Oof!"

Artie lost hold of the board and it fell down, landing with a thump. It just missed Benjie, who jumped back in the nick of time.

"Couldn't you lift it any higher? I nearly had it."

"I are only so tall, Jack. *You* try holding a plank over your head and see how wiggly it gets."

153

Jack swung down and tried to climb up with the board under his arm, but he couldn't. Then the boys tried tossing the boards up at the limbs, hoping some would catch. That, too, was hopeless. The boards kept falling back with a clatter.

"Maybe it are too tall a tree, Jack."

"That makes it good, Artie. Safe from tigers and rhinos. I've got another idea. Got a rope anywhere?"

Artie nodded.

"Good," said Jack. "Run up and get it, and bring a hammer and nails and any other tools you can find."

Artie scampered up the bank, and in a few minutes returned. He was out of breath, but he had the rope and some tools.

"Okay, Artie," Jack called from up in the tree. "Throw the end of the rope up to me."

Artie made several casts. After many misses, he threw it within reach, and Jack caught it. He slung it up over the next higher branch. The rope was long enough so that one end trailed on the ground. Artie and Benjie looked up at jack with curious expressions on their faces. Jack told them to tie their end of the rope around one of the bigger boards, which they did. Then he quickly and easily hoisted the gently swaying board up into the tree and maneuvered it into place between the crotch of the two tree limbs. Several boards were hoisted up in the same way, and crisscrossed into position. By the time it had begun to turn dark, the floor was done.

Jack and Benjie got scolded for getting home late that night. But they didn't mind, for they had started building the long-dreamed-of clubhouse – which had the extra enchantment of being a treehouse!

## CHAPTER XXVI

# A Wailing Encounter

Another golden Saturday rolled around. Jack, Benjie, and Artie had spent their afternoons after school building a roof for the treehouse and some sides, such as they were. Since no two boards were of the same size or thickness, the treehouse was a crazy patchwork. Bugs could fly in through a thousand gaps. The holes didn't bother the boys because they figured the bugs that flew in could fly out the same way. It didn't matter to them that their design would give an architect the flim-flams or the workmanship sicken a carpenter. To the boys, their treehouse was a dream come true. They had already made elaborate plans for using the treehouse, even planning to sleep in it overnight if and as soon as their folks would let them.

Jack and Benjie had hardly gotten their breakfast under their belts before they were speeding down Academy Street. Their thoughts and talk were all of one thing, which was spending the whole day in their treehouse. Not to miss a glorious minute of it, they had packed their lunch.

Their excitement grew as they came to the end of Dobbin Street and could hear the creek up ahead. Soon they were racing past the old hollow tree and bounding across the swinging bridge. Benjie, less frightened than the first time, sprang right across at Jack's heels without having to hold onto the handrail.

"Shh! Hold up," said Jack, halting so suddenly that Benjie ran into him.

"What is it, Jack?" whispered Benjie.

"I'm not sure, but I think someone's up in our treehouse. Stay here. I'm going to see if I can sneak up on 'em."

Jack darted from one tree to the next and crept up to the v-shaped tree. He looked up at the treehouse. He couldn't see inside. So, quietly, he climbed up to where he could peek in. Now he was certain someone was inside.

"Who's in there?" called Jack, like a sentry challenging an intruder.

"It are only me," came a soft reply. "Me and Fred." Artie opened up the trap door in the floor, and he and Fred peeked out. Jack climbed up through.

"Oh, I'm glad it's you, Artie, I was afraid somebody had broken into our treehouse."

"Are it alright that I showed it to Fred? He came over to play."

"Sure, but if he wants to be in it, he'll have to join our club and be sworn to secrecy. Also, he'll have to give something towards the treehouse like food or things to make it better. Is that agreed, Fred?"

"Agreed," said Fred.

155

"And you swear to keep our treehouse a secret, so help you?"

"So help me," said Fred, with a fancy show of oath taking.

"Good. Did Artie show you all about the treehouse?"

"No. I are only showed him the inside so far, Jack."

"What more is there?" asked Fred.

"Aha. You didn't know there was more, did you? It's a secret, that's why."

"Secret? Show me, Jack."

"Before we do, what can you chip in to join the club? We've worked lots of days to make this treehouse as neat as it is." Jack got a very serious look on his face and Artie put on the same look.

"Well," said Fred, gritting his teeth as he was thinking, "I think I could bring some crackers."

"Crackers! Is that all? How about some equipment? Couldn't you bring any equipment?"

"Like what?"

"Like a flashlight, telescope, radio, or something like that."

"Gee, I don't have any of those things. Won't crackers be enough?"

"Okay. But when you're home, see if you can't bring some kind of equipment to join the club. Something besides just crackers."

Then from outside came a sound. A kind of an "ah-whoo-oo-ing!" sound.

"What's that?" asked Fred.

"Oh, my gosh. I forgot all about Benjie. That's our secret coyote signal."

"Sounded more like a sick cow to me," said Fred.

"Watch. I'll show you one of our great inventions. See out this window?"

"Window?" Where's the glass?"

"Don't ask goofy questions, Fred, just watch."

Jack reached out through the hole in the wall and took hold of a rope and began lowering away a board that looked something like the seat of a swing. Then he looked down to the ground and called out to Benjie:

"You on? Okay. Artie, hoist away. Give him a hand, will you Fred? Whatever you do, don't let go. You see, Benjie is too small to reach the first branch so we have to haul him up."

"Isn't that a great elevator?" said Jack to Fred.

"Fred had to admit that it was, but he was smiling to himself.

"What's so funny, Fred?" demanded Jack.

"Oh, it's nothing wrong with your elevator. I was just wondering what it'd pull like with Tubby Suggs on it."

"He are so big, the rope'd break," laughed Artie.

"Show me what else you got, Jack."

"Well, you saw the trapdoor in the floor. Now see if you can spot the secret one in the ceiling."

Fred squinched up his eyes and studied the ceiling.

"You don't see it, do you? You give up?"

Finally, after scanning the top another minute, Fred had to give in. Jack reached for a block of wood overhead and slid back a board which made a cleverly hidden door.

"This leads to our lookout tower. Watch where I put my foot and climb up after me," said Jack."

The boys so enjoyed the view from high up on their tower that later, around noon, sitting like four fire rangers, they unpacked their lunches and ate up there. During lunch, they loafed and invited reverie. They imagined all kinds of terrific things to add to their treehouse hideaway. Things for comfort and protection from bad weather. Things like fantastic signal devices and super-secret compartments to hide stuff. Things to defend themselves from enemy attacks and drive away dinosaurs, foreign invaders, and space monsters. In their imaginations, the treehouse sometimes became a castle turret, a pioneer stockade, a pilot house, a submarine, or a space capsule. It had no limits on air, land, or sea. Whatever their fancy lit on, that's what the treehouse became - quicker than Cinderella's pumpkin changed to a carriage.

The trek into fantasy might have gone on uninterrupted, if Artie hadn't looked toward Creek Street. From their high point on top of the treehouse they had a good view of the sidewalk on either side of the street.

"Hey look! Are that Fatima Swarts over there?"

"I think you're right," said Fred. "And isn't that Sue and Jennifer walking with her?"

All the boys turned their eyes in that direction and strained to make out who it was. Jack seemed most interested of all, but said nothing.

"It are hard to tell if that's Sue or not," said Artie.

"Yeah, they don't call her 'toothpicks' for nothing. But I'd recognize Fatima a mile away. Fats is harder to hide than a missile base. You want to go over and see them?" asked Fred.

Jack didn't have to be asked twice. He was the first one to reach the ground, swinging down by one great swoop on what the boys called their Tarzan rope.

Fatima, Sue, and Jennifer were delighted to see the boys, and stopped to kid around with them. The boys jostled each other and wise-cracked, all except Benjie who kept yawning and was bored by it all. Finally, the boys couldn't resist showing the girls the swinging bridge. Of course, they leaped on it with great daring and recklessness while the girls screamed and shrieked. All considered, the girls were good sports about it, even though going over the trembling footbridge really put a scare into them. Jennifer took the bouncing on the swinging bridge much like a passenger on a carnival ride who is bobbed around, but expects at the end of the ride to land safely. There were moments when the bridge might have bottomed out with Fatima's added weight, but everyone was too caught up in the fun to worry about a steel cable breaking. When, finally, they were on solid ground once more, they sighed and laughed and caught their breath. It was then that the joy of the moment stopped abruptly. Not one, but *all* of them seemed to notice a new disturbing dark presence, as if a storm cloud had suddenly formed.

Across the street were three boys. And warm though it was, they wore the black jackets of their rat-pack gang.

"Jack," said Jennifer, in a low voice as she raised her fingers to her lips in surprise. "It's Jasper!"

Nobody knew what the three boys intended to do. They only stood with cold curiosity, and looked across the street at the opposite curb where the three boys gawked back at them. No one moved more than a shiver at the icy looks that greeted them across the width of the street. Jasper was in the center. And his creepy sidekicks, Luke and Matt, were bolstering him up like a couple of bookends. The rat-faced one kept looking nervously to his piggy-faced leader as if waiting for orders. Jasper was the first to speak. Although his words were directed to Luke, he obviously intended them to be overheard.

"Look, ain't that Jerk over there?" sneered Jasper.

The mossy-toothed kid grinned awfully.

"It's gotta be Jerky. Course, I might be mistaken. It might be a bunch o' squirrels, a bunch o' *tree* squirrels!"

Rat-face took up the refrain. "Yeah, lookit the buncha squirrels, buncha squirrels!"

"Yeah?" Jack called back. "It's better being a squirrel than a bunch of nutheads like you."

Scared as they were, the girls couldn't help giggling at Jack's reply, and he managed a little smile himself. Jasper's piggy face turned more sour. He brought out a switch-blade knife and began opening and closing the blade over and over again.

"Jerky don't know that squirrel's kin be skinned. Does he, boys?"

"Yeah?" Jack answered him back. "And nuts like you can be cracked, too!"

Several tense minutes passed while words of abuse were hurled back and forth across the street. In the meantime, Jack's group had armed themselves with rocks and mud balls, with Benjie's help, to protect themselves, just in case Jasper made any move toward them with his knife. Seeing it was a standoff and his sidekicks were getting twitchy, Jasper decided to back down. Not, however, without casting one last chilling look over his shoulder before strutting off down the street – his creepy sidekicks slithering close after.

When Jasper and his rats were out of sight, Jack, Fred, Artie, and Benjie discussed what had happened with the girls. After a time, it seemed safe. So the girls headed up the street going in the opposite direction from Jasper. The boys waved goodbye to them, glancing now and then down the street to be sure that Jasper was not in hiding or sneaking up on them. When the girls had gone, the boys headed to the treehouse. It was then, before crossing over the swinging bridge, that the boys looked up and realized that their treehouse could easily be seen from across the street, since the leaves were not fully out yet.

"Do you think Jasper knows about our treehouse?" Benjie asked the question, although it was clearly on everyone's mind.

"I'm not sure," said Jack. After all the work building it, he shuddered at the thought of losing their treehouse as they had lost their go-cart.

"It are strange that he'd say what he did, if he didn't know about it, don't you think?" said Artie.

"You mean about squirrels, tree squirrels?"

"That are it."

"How come Jasper always wants to boss everyone and make trouble, Jack?"

159

"I don't know, Benjie. What's worse, there are creeps dumb enough to follow him. I think maybe we'd better hold a meeting soon to figure out some strategy, in case they come back and try to make trouble for us."

It was suppertime and the boys left for home, but not without first tossing all the good mud ball ammunition that Benjie had collected for them. They took great delight in splattering mud balls all over some made-up targets which they called Jasper's rats. After that, the boys felt much better, especially when Artie, in his own unique way, proudly announced:

"Let 'em come. I are ready for 'em."

CHAPTER XXVII

# Battle Plans Drawn Up

Sunday afternoon, the boys met back at the treehouse. It was a mild, overcast day. From up on the roof of the treehouse or the lookout tower, as they called it, they could see over the tops of the houses on Creek Street. In some of the backyards were fruit trees in blossom, which from their height looked like popcorn trees. The boys sat comfortably munching on crackers.

"Glad you remembered to bring these crackers, Fred, but couldn't you bring any equipment?" asked Jack.

"I asked my folks, but they wouldn't let me bring our radio. And we don't have a telescope, or anything, to chip in. Don't you have any equipment of your own?"

Fred, head down, hands sunk deep into his pockets, suddenly brightened. He excitedly fidgeted with his pockets. Then from their depths, he brought out a handful of stuff.

"How about some of my treasures?" he asked.

"Let's see what you've got there," said Jack.

Fred, looking on proudly, spread out a handful of his pocket treasures in the center of the group.

Benjie's eyes sparkled with interest as he leaned forward to get a better look, while Artie, google-eyed, gazed at the pile. Jack was curious, but kept cool about it.

"Stop gaping so, Artie," said Jack. "Don't you carry stuff in *your* pockets?"

Artie pulled his pockets inside out.

"There are *holes* in 'em," he said.

"Well, what do you think?" said Fred, his hopes rising. "Am I a full-fledged member now?"

Jack reached through the tangle of string, bolts, and bottle caps and lifted up a red and black yo-yo.

"That's a 'champeen' yo-yo, Jack. I worked it forty-seven times once."

Jack tried it. Holding the string loop on his finger, he sailed the yo-yo down and up, down and up. After that, he put the yo-yo back and dipped into the pile once more. "What's so special about this whistle?"

Fred cleared his throat. "I thought that'd make a good signal. I traded Sam four of my best baseball cards for it. See? It's an official Dick Tracy police whistle. Let me show you"

Fred puffed up with air and sent a big blast through the whistle – Brr-l-rr-l-reet!
"There, isn't that neat?"

"Sure is loud, I'll say that," said Jack, plugging his ears.

"How about it, Jack? Am I in the club now?"

"This is a democratic club, Fred. We'll have to vote on you. Get inside the treehouse while we vote."

Fred climbed down through the secret door while the boys put their heads together. When their meeting was over and they had voted, they called him back up on the lookout tower. Jack was the first to shake Fred's hand.

"Welcome into the club, Number 003. From now on, that's your secret agent number. Benjie's 002, I'm 001…"

"…and I are Oh-Oh-Oh," said Artie.

Fred was all smiles as he shook hands with Artie and Benjie.

"Now," said Jack, "to the next order of business. We've got to have a strategy meeting to be ready for Jasper, in case he and his rats ever show up here again."

"You sure Jasper knows about the treehouse and are out to get us, Jack?"

"I don't know, Artie. But he's already been spying around here. And one other time, I had a fight with him and his gang. You can take my word on it – there's nothing he likes better than picking on someone, especially when his gang outnumbers them. Fred, here, knows. He lives near Jasper or Casper or whatever you want to call him, and he can tell you how he bullies all the kids in the neighborhood."

"Yeah, especially kids littler than him," said Fred.

"So, last night before going to bed, I jotted down every strategy I could think of." Jack brought out a folded sheet of paper and snapped it open. "Here they are. Now don't laugh because I thought seriously about these, all fifteen of 'em. So, listen and listen closely."

*STRATEGY TO PROTECT OUR TREEHOUSE IN CASE OF ATTACK.*

*COURSES OF ACTION:*
    *1.  Give in and let Jasper be boss of it.*

"Give in?! Let Jasper be boss?! Jeepers, Jack!"
"Hold your horses, Benjie, will you? I said these were *possible* choices. I didn't say which one we'd do. Let me finish and don't butt in. Then we'll decide."

    *2.  Let Jasper and his gang use it when they want to.*
    *3.  Wreck the treehouse ourselves before they get a chance to.*
    *4.  Ask to join Jasper's gang or try to make peace with them.*
    *5.  Make Jasper see he's doing wrong, doing what he does.*
    *6.  Tell them we won't do nothing to them if they won't do nothing to us or else give them something to leave us alone.*
    *7.  Try to forget them and hope they leave us alone.*

"That are just like doing nothin'," muttered Artie. Jack looked crossly, then continued reading.

    *8.  Get more guys in our club or maybe join forces with other clubs in town.*
    *9.  Put booby-traps around the treehouse.*
  *10.  Get stuff to fight back with and maybe they'll be scared away.*
  *11.  Make our treehouse stronger so if they do come to bother us, we'll be safe inside it.*
  *12.  Pretend we've got a secret weapon in the treehouse and talk it up how strong our gang is and warn them to stay away.*
  *13.  Try to get Jasper's rats to quit his club and help our side.*
  *14.  Beat Jasper to the punch and attack him first.*
  *15.  Get the police to protect us and maybe have them throw Jasper and his goons in jail.*

By the time Jack had finished reading the long list, Benjie was rubbing his hands furiously. "Let's get the police to throw Jasper in jail, Jack!"

"That'd be great all right, but they haven't wrecked the treehouse yet. And how are we going to prove they've done anything wrong?" said Jack.

Benjie looked stunned.

"You mean there's no law or police to protect us against hoods like Jasper?"

"I don't think the police would think a treehouse was important enough to protect," said Fred. "A big house, sure, but a small treehouse, no. What about your dad, Artie? Would he help us?"

"He are too busy with TV. Anyhow, how are we gonna prove we belong here? Except we built this treehouse, we don't even know who owns this land."

For several minutes more, the boys studied the list and nobody said anything. First one, then another, would seem to come alive with an idea, but then sink back into thought. Fred kept pursing his lips while Artie scratched his head, and Benjie idly fiddled with some of Fred's pocket treasures.

"If you can think of something not on the list, go ahead and say it," said Jack.

"Nobody got any ideas? Gee, I wish my Uncle Ollie was here. Bet he'd have some ideas. I guess all we can do is go down the list and decide something from that. I take it from what Benjie said that nobody's willing to just give in to Jasper and let him take over. And I guess we can cross out the last one about getting the police to help us. What about some of the other possibilities?"

"Knowing the things Jasper does in his own neighborhood, I don't think any of the points up to number 7 would work," said Fred.

"Okay. If everyone agrees with that, I'll cross 'em off. How about number 8 – getting more guys in our club?" asked Jack.

"That seems good. Maybe we could get Billy or Rodney or…"

"Yeah," said Benjie with a gleam in his eye. "I'll bet Rodney could chip in some neat equipment."

"But would Rodney stick by us and fight if Jasper attacks?"

For a minute, nobody spoke. Benjie went back to fiddling with Fred's bottle caps.

"How about Billy, then?" asked Fred.

"Only thing is, if we make Billy a member, then his cousin Tubby would probably want to join, too. And I don't know whether the treehouse could support three more guys – and Tubby, too."

"Huh," snickered Artie. "With Tubby in the treehouse, the club wouldn't have room for no members but him."

"Yeah. Besides, did you ever see how much he eats? We wouldn't be able to get food enough to feed him" said Jack.

The boys had a good laugh, thinking of all the things that might happen with Tubby in the treehouse. As the stories got bigger, so did Tubby. Finally, Jack settled them down to serious discussion again. They crossed out all the numbers about attacking Jasper first, or trying to bluff him and having nothing to back it up.

"Let's see now," said Jack. "That leaves 9, 10, and 11 – putting booby-traps around, having stuff to fight with, and making the treehouse stronger. Which ones of these can we cross off?"

The boys, again, got very thoughtful going over each point carefully. Finally, since nobody offered any suggestions, Jack called on Fred to speak his mind on it.

"Gee, I don't know, Jack. It might be good if we make the treehouse stronger. Only thing is, we couldn't be around to guard it all the time, or stay in it all the time, either. There's no way of knowing what Jasper might do. He always acts so crummy."

"What do you think, Artie?" asked Jack.

"How about making up a stink bomb like that time at Rodney's?"

"The trouble is – even if we could mix the same stuff, none of us have a chemistry set."

"Still, I think it are important to have stuff to fight Jasper off with."

"Yeah," said Benjie. "He could be sneaking up on us right now. We should have something to clobber Casper good, like a custard pie right in the puss."

"Oh, I wouldn't waste a good pie on that rat," said Fred.

"Oh, me neither," giggled Benjie. "Not unless the pie was real rotten."

"Hey, yeah, Jack. Where could we get some rotten pies?"

For the rest of that day and several days following, Jack, Artie, Fred, and Benjie worked on the defenses for their treehouse. They checked at the bakery, but couldn't get any old rotten pies unless they paid for them. So, they settled instead for mud pies, which they make themselves by the side of the creek. To shoot the pies, Jack hit upon the idea of building a catapult, like he'd learned about from studying the history of the Middle Ages. It was made of a one inch board 2 ½ feet long, that pivoted on a rusty hinge. A piece of old rubber inner tube served as the spring mechanism. The board held down with a mud pie on the end when released would shoot the pie forward. They mounted their catapult on top of the lookout tower and it pivoted so they could fire mud pies as far as the swinging bridge.

Then Jack hit upon a plan for a warning system. He'd seen a similar idea in a war movie. Instead of barbed wire, the boys' warning system was made of kite string, tin cans, and pebbles. The boys dirtied the string and camouflaged it as much as possible, while stringing it between trees and across most of the paths leading to the treehouse. From the ground, the string hung about knee-high at its highest point to ankle-high at its lowest. Between each tree, the string was threaded through two, three, or four tin cans. Several pebbles were placed in each can. As Jack showed them, someone coming along and not seeing the string would trip over it. When the string was disturbed or broken, it would set the tin cans to rolling and clattering, sounding the alarm. Since the treehouse club members knew where the string was, all they had to do to avoid setting off the alarms, was to be careful to step over it each time.

Finally, since the hollow tree was a good hiding place and guarded the path to the swinging bridge, the boys decided to make it a special advance outpost. In a crevice inside the tree, they hid one of Fred's donations to the treehouse club – the Dick Tracy whistle. Whoever was standing guard at the outpost could warn the treehouse when an enemy approached by a blast on the whistle.

"See," said Fred proudly, when he saw they had found use for the Dick Tracy whistle. "I told you that whistle was good equipment."

"Yeah," said Artie in his own special way of speaking, "but what good are a yo-yo?"

CHAPTER XXVIII

# Night in the Treehouse

For many days, the boys gloried in their treehouse fortress. Their spirits were high and they were very alert, keeping a constant lookout for the Jasper gang. They played war games practicing how they would fend off an enemy attack. When no attack came, little by little they relaxed. They were tired of watching. They were bored with waiting. The suspense of not knowing if they would be attacked made them edgy and restless. Sometimes they almost wished something would happen so they would no longer have to worry. Gradually, the memory of Jasper's piggy-face slid out of their minds altogether, and they started to squabble among themselves. Some of the arguments nearly cause the treehouse club to split up.

The two things which caused the most trouble were the hollow tree and the catapult. None of the members liked to stand guard in the hollow tree because it was uncomfortable and lonely, compared with being up in the treehouse. Besides, it was the most dangerous spot because you were by yourself and wide-open to attack. The second big cause of argument was the catapult. Since it was their most powerful weapon, all the members wanted to be in charge of it. Fred made a strong case for himself by saying that he had made a lot of the mud pies. And if all members were equal, he should have just as much right to fire it as anyone. But Jack finally won out because, as he argued, he had thought of the catapult, made it, and obviously could be more trusted using it than anybody else.

The June days lengthened into weeks. During all the weeks of work on the treehouse, Jack found little time to see Jennifer. One day during school, he learned through Sue, who told Fatima, who told Billy, who then told Jack, that Jennifer had something to tell him. When school let out, he met her at her locker.

"Can I carry something for you?"

"Thanks, Jack. Really, I can manage. I wouldn't want to put you to any trouble."

"It's no trouble. Watch this." Jack put Jennifer's notebook on his chin and balanced it with his arms stretched out like a juggler. Jennifer smiled a tiny bit. Jack just caught the notebook as it started to fall.

"I'll bet you were afraid I'd drop it, weren't you?"

"No, no, I wasn't thinking of that."

"Well, I can't say that I might not, someday. Nobody's perfect, you know, not even me."

Outside, the brilliant sunlight made them blink their eyes. The sidewalk glared white against the green lawn. Children were climbing aboard the bright yellow-orange school buses that lined the school driveway. The blacktop pavement seemed to quiver with the heat waves.

"I'll bet you've been wondering what I've been doing lately," said Jack.

"Yes, yes, I have wondered. You haven't been around much."

"Well, it's been kind of a secret, but I can tell you. We've formed a club and built a treehouse, Benjie, Artie, Fred, and myself. Only don't tell them that I told you, because it's a secret. I've got some other good news, too, that I haven't told anybody yet."

Jack spun the notebook between his fingers. He was clearly delighted about something.

"What is…your good news?"

"Tonight, my folks are going to let me sleep out overnight in the treehouse. Of course, they could change their minds, yet. But if they let me, it'll be about the most exciting thing that ever happened to me. Imagine it – camping overnight in a treehouse!"

Jack walked along as if his head was almost up in the clouds. He was so caught up in the thought of it that he almost forgot he was with Jennifer.

"Who's going to camp out with you?"

"Hmm? Well, all of us want to. But I don't think Benjie's folks will let him because he littler. So it'll probably be Artie, Fred, and me."

The conversation didn't last long, before they arrived at Jennifer's house. Turning up her front walk, Jack noticed a little real estate sign in the center of the lawn. On the sign printed in clear letters were the words – FOR SALE. Jennifer had slowed her pace. And when they stood at the steps leading to her front door, she stopped and faced Jack.

"Jack, I…I have something to tell you."

As Jack looked into her eyes, he could see that she was struggling to say what she had to. Before she spoke, she turned her eyes away and brushed back a lock of hair from her forehead.

"Jack, my father's been transferred. We're moving to Columbus, Ohio."

"You're what?" Jack was struck dumb. His thoughts were like words stuck in his throat.

'When?" he asked.

"Tomorrow. Will you ever forget me?"

"No. I'll never…"

Before Jack cold finish, Jennifer suddenly grabbed her notebook, kissed Jack on the cheek, and disappeared into her house.

Jack remembered very little of what happened after that. He couldn't remember walking home, or sitting down at the table, or even what was served for supper.

After supper, Jack shuffled down Elm Street. Jennifer's news had made him blue. Arriving at the treehouse, he set down his bulky bed roll which he'd carried along slung over his shoulder, and called up to Artie:

"Lower down the elevator."

Artie looked out through the bottom trapdoor. Then he scratched his head.

"You kidding, Jack? I aren't strong enough to lug you up here."

"I know that. All I want you to do is haul up my sleeping bag."

"Oh sure, Jack. Are Benjie coming, too?"

"No. His folks wouldn't let him. It looks like it'll just be you, Fred, and me."

"Correction, Jack. Me and you. Fred couldn't camp out, either."

Artie helped Jack roll out his sleeping bag. At home, they hardly ever made their own beds, except maybe when their mothers nagged them to. But in the treehouse, it was different. There was an excitement about it, like being an explorer in a jungle of your very own. With their bedding all laid out and smoothed, the boys just had to stand back in admiration. The small space in the treehouse made it all the more cozy. The boys decided next to explore along the creek bank to maybe discover some gold or pirate's treasure chest. They swung down out of their treehouse on their 'Tarzan' rope.

"Careful," said Jack, as they walked down a path toward the creek. "Don't' trip over any of our string alarms."

The boys walked along the bank. The air was filled with birdcalls and the rippling music of the creek. Each step they took was answered back by the scrunch of dry twigs and leaves. On the way, they swung on some vines and balanced over fallen tree logs. At the edge of the creek, they jumped down on the drystones that bordered the running stream. The dusty stones shifted, scraped, and clattered beneath their feet. Jack skipped a flat stone over the surface of the water. Artie followed this by lobbing in a small round boulder. It landed with such a big SPLASH that it sent up a huge geyser. The boys had to jump back or be splattered. They laughed and joked about it.

Next, Jack leaped out on the farthest steppingstone he could in one jump. Artie, not taking any chances of getting his feet wet, squatted at the water's edge. The swirling creek was an endless show with water bugs skittering over the calm sidewash, bits of twigs sailing downstream, and minnows nosing against the current. As evening approached, the stones turned orange and the long shadows of the trees stretched across the width of the creek. The boys headed back to the treehouse, and climbed up on their lookout tower to watch the sun set.

"What's that you popped into your mouth, Artie?" asked Jack.

"Oh, this? It are candy. I meant to tell you, but it slipped my mind. One of Jasper's gang give it to me this afternoon. I think they're trying to make friends with us. Here, have some."

Jack took a piece of the candy in his hand and gasped.

"What's the matter? Are it dirty or something?"

"Artie, how much of this have you eaten?"

"Oh, I don't know. I got a lot left yet. Why?"

"Don't eat anymore. That's not regular candy. That's a laxative!"

It wasn't long before Artie excused himself and dashed up the hill toward his house. Jack called after Artie to look at home for a flashlight, but he was in such a hurry, he never looked back. He raced away in what must have been record time for running cross-country. While Jack waited, he lay back and relaxed on the lookout tower, his head cradled in his hands. He could hear the night songs of the birds guarding their nests. The shadows slowly deepened till everything appeared to lose color. The leaves quivered gently against the night sky like a shadow play. Jack watched the first stars blossom out in the twilight sky and listened as the night air became charged with the songs of frogs croaking and crickets chirping.

It seemed to Jack as he waited, that Artie was taking an awfully long time. It was getting cool. Jack pulled on his sweater against the chill, damp-night air. Suddenly he was startled to hear a clanking noise. It was immediately followed by some mumbling. Jack tried to pierce the darkness with his eyes, but it was too thick. He stopped breathing to listen better. "Ha. Clumsy Artie probably tripped over one of our warning strings and jangled some of the tin cans," Jack thought to himself. "Or maybe he's just trying to fool me. Could be a dog, too. But then," thought Jack, as he heard more twigs snap, "dogs don't usually make noise when they walk." Jack was tempted to call out, but then thought better of it. For if it wasn't Artie that would give away his hiding place. Jack thought about using the catapult, but decided against that because he had no way of seeing who he was firing at, whether he would be hitting enemy or friend. From the height of the lookout tower he couldn't make out what was on the ground, nor could he see directly beneath the treehouse. Jack decided to climb down into the treehouse and continue his watch through the trapdoor. He wished that Fred could have chipped in a flashlight as part of the equipment for the club. Then again, shining a flashlight out of the treehouse would be sure to give it away. Whereas, someone not knowing about the treehouse could easily walk by the v-shaped tree without ever seeing it in the dark. It was at just that instant that Jack heard the unmistakable scrape of a shoe scuffling against bark. In the dense gloom below he could just make out the movement of three dark figures. One of them was beginning to climb the tree. A patch of mottled light played across one of the upturned faces. It was Jasper.

Jack clenched his fists. He knew he had to do something and do it quick. The tree-dwellers had planned well at first, how together they would fight off an attack, but then they had gotten careless and wasted their time arguing. Now Jack was left to fight off the rat-pack gang all alone. There was no time to feel sorry for himself. His mind raced across possibilities. What had they hidden in their secret compartment? Jack opened it. There was only some string, bottle-caps, and Fred's yo-yo. Jack got an idea.

He grabbed the yo-yo and crawled over to the open trapdoor. He put his finger through the string loop and clutched the yo-yo in his hand, peering over the edge. Luke was clawing his way slowly up the tree. When he was near enough, Jack sailed the yo-yo down at Luke. It missed, but passed spider-like so near Luke's face that it startled him, for he lost his grip and plunged half way down the tree.

"What's the matter, ya clod," hissed Jasper in a loud whisper.

"I don't know. Something came after me," murmured Luke.

"Git back up there! You too, Matt. Stop being so chicken or you'll get worse from me."

Again, when they were within range, Jack sailed the yo-yo down. This time it clonked Matt on the head.

"Yow!" he bellowed.

"Hey, shush up you clowns. Do you want to tip 'em off we're here?" said Jasper.
"Somethin' just bopped me on the head."

"Watch out where you're going. You probably bumped into a branch."

Because the last yo-yo shot hit Matt, the string tangled so that it didn't reel back up. Jack saw all too well that he wouldn't have time to rewind it before they would be in the treehouse.

Quickly he closed the trapdoor. He was breathing hard now but he could still hear them talking outside.

"Hey, Jasper, one of 'em is up in there."

"Good! We got 'im trapped. Get 'im."

"But he closed the door."

"Ya dumb oafs. The two of ya pushing against it should be able to open it."

Jack sat on the door. He could feel them pushing up against it and hear them grunting. He began to feel sure that he could hold out against them because they were trying to push up against gravity and his weight, besides. If it hadn't been so serious, Jack probably would have laughed at them, but he didn't have the chance. Just at that moment, he heard some thumping and shuffling overhead. He looked up through the open door to the lookout tower. In the opening, leering down at him was Jasper's piggy face. Jack could not shut the overhead door now. Nor could he get off the trapdoor without letting Luke and Matt in. Jack wondered what on earth he could do next.

CHAPTER XXIX

# The Battle Concluded

Jack's heart was thumping like a tom-tom. Trapped in the treehouse, Luke and Matt shoving at the trapdoor from underneath, and Jasper glaring down from overhead through the open lookout tower door – all seemed hopeless. Jack knew if he didn't hold down the lid of the trapdoor, Jasper's goons would climb up in the treehouse. Even if he could stop Luke and Matt from getting in, he would have to stand off Jasper.

Every time Luke and Matt rammed against the trapdoor, the door bumped up, and Jack tromped down on it hard. Now he was forced to turn around and crouch on the door to keep a better eye on Jasper. There wasn't much else he could do until Jasper made his next move. He decided to hold off Jasper's sidekicks as long as he could. If Jasper wanted to fight, he'd have to come after Jack by himself.

Luke and Matt continued pushing and grunting.

"Can't you see who's in there?" one of them called up to Jasper.

It was dark in the treehouse so Jasper had to squint to see inside. Framed in the opening, his piggy face stood out against a patch of night sky. Jack couldn't help thinking how the stars shining down through that small but big chunk of space must have seen a lot of nights, nights of dreamy sleep, and nights of storm, and still they sparkled on and looked as peaceful as ever.

"Didn't ya see who's in there yet?" Luke asked.

"He's gotta weigh at least a ton," said Matt.

He and Luke were breathing hard from pushing up against the trapdoor. The door wasn't jumping up and banging as much as it had at first.

"Why you weak-kneed dumbheads. Put your shoulders to it and push. It's only Jerky inside there. Push!"

"What's he think we been trying to do?" Jack heard Matt mumble to Luke.

"Push, you lunkheads!" Jasper kept screaming commands from up above while his two creepy sidekicks kept ramming themselves against the trapdoor with no luck. Jasper went on yelling advice or calling Luke and Matt names but made no move himself to come down into the treehouse, although he could have easily. The pushing stopped when Luke got his hand pinched in the door and let out a howl. It looked as if Jack, outnumbered as he was, had battled them to a draw, unless Jasper tried something.

Jack didn't have long to enjoy this standoff before he heard Jasper call over the side: "Luke, come on up here."

"Let Matt come. My hand hurts," answered Luke.

Jasper evidently had hit upon some new plan. Whatever it was, Jack wanted to be sure that one of the gang was really going to join Jasper on the lookout tower. Apparently, Luke was nursing his pinched hand because the trapdoor stopped jiggling. Jack could hear the shuffling of someone climbing up the side of the treehouse. While he listened, he was surprised to hear another loud, shrill noise. It went *Brrr-lrr-l-reet!*

At first, Jack was puzzled. But when the sound came for the second time, he recognized it as being part of Fred's donation to the treehouse club. It was the Dick Tracy police whistle that the boys had hidden in the hollow tree.

*'What would crazy Artie be blowing the warning whistle now for'*, thought Jack. He didn't have long to wonder before he heard a lot of scrambling overhead.

"Did ya hear that whistle? Get outta my way, Matt. Move! Move! It's the cops!"

Jack could hear Jasper and Matt scuffling, bumping, and grumbling at each other as they climbed down over the side of the treehouse. Jack lifted the trapdoor cautiously and peeked out. He was just in time to see Luke already down and running. Next, he saw Jasper and Matt drop from the tree. In their hurry to get away, they turned and ran smack into each other, and tumbled to the ground.

"You dumb dope!" bellowed Jasper. "Get out of my way." With that, he shoved Matt in the face and got back on his feet and ran. Matt quickly picked himself up and took off, too. Jack couldn't see anything more, so he climbed up on the lookout tower. Except for the streetlight over on Creek Street, it was too dark to see much of anything among the trees. All he could do was hear the crunch of their feet running through twigs and brush. But shortly to this a new sound was added – a loud ear-rapping clatter! It was the sound of tin cans clinking and clanking. Jack soon guessed that Jasper's gang had gotten themselves tangled up in every string trap that the treehouse club had laid out all the way to the swinging bridge. In the darkness, Jack could just make out one of the gang bounding across the bridge trailing a string of rattling tin cans behind him.

Then the noise stopped, and all was very still. Even the frogs, birds, and crickets had stopped their serenading during all the commotion. Jack decided to go search for Artie. He swung down to the ground on the 'Tarzan' rope and looked around

The night creatures took up their songs again as Jack picked his way along the path toward the swinging bridge. Walking along, he brushed aside branches that criss-crossed the path. The leaves felt cool and damp to his hands. Jack stopped at a sound, but then decided that the noise had only been the slap of a sapling along the path. When he stood at the ramp leading onto the swinging bridge, Jack saw someone standing across the creek between the two upright poles from which the bridge cables were strung. It was impossible to make out who it was in the dark.

"Artie?" Jack called out.

"Are that you, Jack?" A blinding glare of light made Jack shield his eyes. Then the flashlight's circle came at Jack with its beam dancing merrily.

Artie came bouncing over the swinging bridge on the double. His face was weirdly shadowed and pasty-white behind the light, but otherwise a big grin stretched clear across his face.

"Are you okay?" asked Artie.

"Yeah. What about you?"

"I hid in the hollow tree while a couple of them ran by." Artie turned his head from side to side and watched the bushes.

"How come you blew the warning whistle? That *was* you, wasn't it?"

"It were me alright. See, it happened like this. When I come out of my house and was heading back to the treehouse, I saw what looked like Jasper and his creeps around the tree. For a minute, I thought they'd heard me 'cause I made some noise and they looked my way. So I froze and thought over what to do next. Then I remembered how we'd planned to blow the warning whistle in case of attack. So I sneaked down the bank and over the swinging bridge to the hollow tree and got the whistle."

"Boy, it's a lucky thing you did. Jasper's creeps were trying to bust into the treehouse. But the minute they heard the whistle, they thought the police were after them."

"Oh," laughed Artie, "so that are why Luke and Matt tore over the swinging bridge dragging along all them tin cans."

The boys headed back to the treehouse. From under the gray dome of the sky, they headed into the dark woods. The creek kept up its sing-song flowing.

"What about Jasper?" asked Jack, as they walked along together. "Did you see Jasper run by?"

Artie didn't have time to answer, before they both saw something halfway up the trail. A lone figure was cowering in the shadows by a tree. It was Jasper! Jack took the stance of a cowboy gunfighter. This time the tables were turned – Jasper's way was blocked. Jack took the flashlight from Artie and pointed it up the path. The strong beam of the light fell full across Jasper's face. His piggy eyes stared back at the light with the look of a trapped animal. His mouth fell open, when he realized the light was on him. Suddenly, he darted off the path and ran. Jack and Artie could hear him tripping and crashing through the tangled vines and brambles.

"Where'd he go?" whispered Artie.

"From the sound of it, he's down near the creek." Jack pointed the flashlight toward the creek bank, sweeping it's beam gradually along till it played off the back of Jasper's black jacket. Artie was first to see him and called out:

"There he are! He's in the creek!"

The last Jack and Artie had seen of him, Jasper was wading across the creek, slipping and splashing till he came out on the other side, thoroughly soaked and looking for all the world like a drenched rat.

Later, when the boys figured they'd seen the last of Jasper's gang for the night, they climbed up into their treehouse beds and discussed the battle.

"Why didn't you blast 'em with the catapult, Jack?"

"Couldn't chance it with you out there, Artie."

So, there'd been no opportunity to use their most awesome weapon. Jack guessed that was the weakness of super weapons – they lacked discrimination in mixed battle, being no more choosey between friend or foe than the weather.

"What a skunk that Jasper are. I'll bet he grows up to be a crook."

"He's pretty rotten all right. Still, that doesn't mean he couldn't change. Nothing's impossible, you know. Why, he might even grow up to be a preacher or a politician.

"Jasper?"

"Sure. It could happen. Anybody can go either way he wants to. As a matter of fact, it's lots better to be a made-over bad guy, than be a good person who goes wrong. Why, heck, as far as I can see, a guy who hasn't done anything wrong has got a couple of strikes against him. He doesn't have any room to show improvement."

"I s'pose that are so. Uh, huh," agreed Artie yawning.

"Besides, people are more apt to fuss over a bad guy that makes good. I guess they figure he had to make it the hard way."

"Oh, hum," yawned Artie rolling over.

"Come to think of it, haven't you ever noticed how when a bad guy turns good, he usually tries extra hard to make others good? Isn't that funny, Artie?...Artie?"

"Z-Z-Z-z-z-z-z!"

"Well, I'll be darned. He's fallen asleep already."

Finally, aglow with triumph and all snuggled in his tree house bed, Jack, too, fell asleep under the stars.

# Bonus Short Story: What Day is Coming?

Peedie and Jack ran down the sidewalk in the warmth of an April morning. Sun shining through the budding trees cut the sidewalk into puzzle pieces. The children hop-scotched through the shadow lines shouting, "Don't step on a crack or you'll break your mother's back!"

Without winter boots, their feet flew. Without heavy coats, they bounded like gazelles. Of course, Jack could leap two sidewalk blocks to Peedie's twenty skiddle-skaddles because he was in sixth grade and Peedie was in second.

"Hurry up, Peedie!" Jack called back.

Peedie had stubbed his toe on a sidewalk crack and fallen down in front of old Mrs. McCree's house. On his feet again, he dusted himself off and, without a murmur, skipped on. Peedie was a nickname for Philip Douglas Holiday, a very large name for such a little fellow. So, his family called him by his first initials. Thus, "Peedie."

"You almost rolled in old Mrs. McCree's flower bed. Then we'd sure get heck," said Jack. Sometimes Peedie was a bother to Jack. When they played sandlot baseball, Peedie would usually end up on Jack's team. Peedie was what the kids called an "easy out." If he hit the ball instead of striking out, he was lucky to get to base. Once, Peedie *might* have made first base, having finally hit the ball well, but as luck would have it, he became so excited he slung his bat through the neighbors' picture window. Peedie made it to base all right, but all the other kids ran off and left him standing on first base.

"Don't be so pokey," said Jack, as Peedie continued to lag behind.

"Peedie! Jack!" came a shrill call. "Wait for me." The boys turned to see their sister skipping after them. Nancy was between Jack and Peedie and was a fourth grader. Nancy no longer took much interest in playing with her brothers. Her interests were horses and dolls and, as Jack said, "giggling with her silly friends." Jack, Nancy, and Peedie got along as well as most brothers and sisters with time out for an occasional scrap. Like the time the boys' soldiers captured Nancy's dolls and bombed her dollhouse. Mother soon stepped in to stop the war. Jack and Peedie were forced to retreat with their soldiers and repair the damage.

"Say, do you know what day is coming?" Nancy asked. Nancy had a way of dangling a question before her brothers and holding back the answer. Jack always fell for it because he loved to be challenged by questions and hated to be told anything by his sister.

"Sure. Sunday."

"I mean a special day," said Nancy.

"Let's see," said Jack thinking.

"April Fool's Day?" piped up Peedie.

"No," laughed Nancy with a skip. "That was over four weeks ago."

Peedie grinned. "My birthday?"

Nancy shook her head and skipped on.

"You were born in February, stoop," said Jack.

"How about fall?" said Peedie.

"Will you be quiet, Peedie, so I can think? It hasn't even been summer yet. Besides, fall is a season, not a special day."

"You want a hint?" teased Nancy.

"No," said Jack. "Let me think. Does this special day come soon?"

"That'd be a hint. Do you want a hint?"

"Well, it could be Christmas, if it doesn't come soon," said Jack. "Does it come soon?"

Nancy nodded. "In May," she said.

"I'll bet it's some crummy TV star's birthday."

"It's not, Jack. Do you give in? You'll never guess."

"Okay, what is it?"

"Mother's Day," said Nancy triumphantly.

"Say, I *had* forgotten. Hold up a minute, you two."

"What, Jack?"

"Listen, I've got an idea. We've never done anything really great for Mom on Mother's Day. My idea is that we should get jobs and pool our savings and buy her something really nice."

"Let's get her a 'Winnie the Pooh' game," said Peedie.

"That's not what mothers like," said Jack.

"I know just the thing," said Nancy.

"What?"

"A bottle of perfume! I saw one at the store with a golden stopper and a pink ribbon bow. Mom would just love it, I know."

"Maybe for once you've got something, Nancy."

"Aw, perfume? Smelly perfume?" Peedie wrinkled his freckled nose.

"Be quiet, Peedie," said Jack. "You're too young to know about what moms like yet. Come on. We've got to find out how much it costs, how much we've got now, how much we need to earn, and we've only a week to do it in. This has got to be kept *secret*, too. You know what I mean, Peedie? No blabbing it all over town."

"How about Dad?" asked Peedie.

"Not even Dad. A surprise has got to be kept secret. And to do this right, I'll keep a record in my notebook just like businessmen do."

Jack's notebook:

# Holidays and Hoopla

### Saturday

|  |  |
|---|---|
| Jack | $0.33 |
| Nancy | $0.26 |
| Peedie | $0.02 |
| Total to Start: | $0.61 |

also penny in Nancy's lucky charm which we'll dig out if needed.

Goal - Perfume for Mom on Mother's Day

|  |  |
|---|---|
| Cost | $6.25 |
| We have | $0.62 |
| Need to earn | $5.63 |

### Sunday

| | |
|---|---|
| Found change under couch cushions | $0.34 |
| Returned Pepsi bottles to store for deposit. | $0.60 |
| Offered to sell rocket gun to Steve for $1.50. No sale | $0.00 |
| Need | $4.69 |

### Monday

| | | |
|---|---|---|
| Mowed lawn, Peedie helped | Earned | $2.00 |
| Sold baseball trading cards to Steve. | | $0.19 |
| Nancy Dusted. | | $0.35 |
| | Need | $2.15 |

### Tuesday

Peedie helped Mrs. McCree across the street.
Thanks but no cash.
Nancy wove a pot holder, but unable to sell it.
Offered Steve rocket gun for $1.25. No sale.

| | |
|---|---|
| Need same as yesterday | $2.15 |

### Wednesday

Second day nothing earned. Gave pep talk.
Peedie grumbled nobody would give him any jobs.

### Thursday

Peedie helped Mrs. McCree work in her flower garden.
Thanks but no cash.
Dad gave us .90¢ for ice cream.

| | | |
|---|---|---|
| Bought gum instead | Saving | $0.65 |
| Nancy traded her favorite Beatles picture | | |
| For Elvis Presley picture and a nickle. | | $0.05 |
| | Total for the day. | $0.70 |
| | Need | $1.45 |

### Friday

| | |
|---|---|
| Peedie traded monsters for Batman mask and 8¢ | $0.08 |
| Nancy folded laundry, earned | $0.25 |
| Steve offered 60¢ for rocket gun. Turned him down. | |
| Hauled pile of newspapers to junk dealer. | $0.50 |
| Total for the day | $0.83 |
| Still need | $0.62 |

Saturday morning came. Tomorrow was Mother's Day. The children had earned all but sixty-two cents of the money needed to buy the perfume. Jack looked at the grass but it didn't need mowing. There was laundry, though, and Nancy was busy helping with that. Peedie was out with his wagon trying to sell dandelions. If they couldn't earn the rest of the money before the store closed today, they wouldn't be able to surprise mother with the perfume on Mother's Day.

Later in the afternoon, Jack came running home with sixty cents. He had sold his rocket gun to Steve. Nancy had earned twenty-five cents for helping with the laundry. And Peedie had earned four cents. He'd sold three bunches of dandelions to Mr. Yeager next door.

"Let's see," said Jack, biting his pencil. "That gives us six dollars and fifty-two cents. Enough to buy the perfume, and some left over to buy a Mother's Day card."

"Will we have to dig the penny out of the lucky charm?" asked Peedie.

"No, we won't have to use the lucky penny," said Jack.

The children raced to town. They bought the perfume with the gold stopper, pink ribbon, and purple satin box. Next, they picked out a beautiful Mother's Day card to go with it. Nancy wondered how she'd be able to keep a straight face and not give away the secret. They all felt that tomorrow would take a long time to come.

"I'm going to carry the perfume."

"No, I want to carry it," said Peedie, tugging on Nancy's arm.

"Hold it!" said Jack. "The only fair way is to switch off carrying the perfume, so everyone gets a turn. Nancy, you carry the perfume for this block. Peedie, you carry it down Mrs. McCree's block. And I'll take it the last block."

This seemed fair to all, so the three started off. At first, they walked as usual. But the delightful thought of tomorrow made them step faster, spring further, and leap higher. Then it happened. They were in the middle of Mrs. McCree's block when Peedie stubbed his toe. The perfume flew out of his hands! There was the sickening wild grab for the flying package followed by a crash, a very little crash, as the package struck the sidewalk.

The children knelt down around it. As the perfume wet through the package, it spotted the sidewalk and a heavy flowery scent rose in the air. No one spoke. Jack felt like hitting Peedie for dropping the perfume, but at the same time he knew the accident could have happened to him or anyone.

"Anyway, we still have the Mother's Day card," said Jack. He knew this wasn't much comfort, but he couldn't think of anything else to say. After Jack and Nancy had walked on, Mrs. McCree looked out her bedroom window and wondered about the little boy who stood staring at the sidewalk.

It was a sunny Sunday for Mother's Day. Jack lay in bed for some time, and Nancy didn't spring out of her bed, either. Peedie had been up and dressed before

Jack noticed him leave. Jack could bear it no longer. He had to tell of his disappointment to someone. He found Dad reading the Sunday paper. He told Dad everything.

Dad lowered the newspaper. "I know how you must feel, Jack. Some things just can't be helped. But Mom's not going to think any the less of you or Nancy or Peedie because of it. As a matter of fact, Mom has been delighted that you've all been so helpful this last week. About the happiest gift to any mother, I guess, is to have good children. By the way, where's Peedie?"

"Gosh, I don't know. He was out of bed before I was up. Didn't you see him this morning?" asked Jack.

"Yes, I saw him go out," Dad said. "Now that I think of it, he did look upset. Why, Jack?"

"Well, Peedie took it pretty hard about dropping the perfume. He cried himself to sleep last night. Didn't he say where he was going?"

"No. Not a word."

"Gosh, you don't think he'd do anything foolish, do you, Dad?

Just then, the door opened quietly and in peeked Peedie.

"Psst. Is Mom in there?" he whispered.

"She's in the kitchen," said Dad.

Peedie came in, concealing something behind his back. His shirt hung out and his shoes were untied and dirty. He grinned like a mouse that got the cheese.

"What've you got there, Peedie?" asked Dad.

Peedie grinned and held up a bouquet of spring flowers. Jack and Dad were almost too surprised to speak. They both knew that the flowers Peedie was holding were not picked in their yard. A horrible thought came to both of them. Jack looked at Dad. Dad looked at Jack. Then they both looked at Peedie.

"Pee—die," said Jack, digging for an answer.

At that moment, Nancy came in. She looked surprised and puzzled. "Where'd the flowers come from?" she asked. "There's only one yard in the whole neighborhood with flowers as pretty as these."

"I was thinking the same thing," said Jack, nodding. Mrs. McCree's yard."

"You didn't,' said Dad.

"Oh, no, Peedie," said Jack.

Peedie hung his head and wiggled his toes. They all looked Peedie in the face. Peedie looked out of the corner of his eye, smelled the flowers, and fidgeted with the stems before he spoke.

"Since I was the one who broke the perfume, I thought I should go out and get a job…"

"And…" said Dad, coaxing.

"…and earn some money. So, I went down the street and I saw Mrs. McCree working in her flower garden. She was the only person outside that early in the morning. So, I asked her if I could help her. Well, just like the other times I worked for her, she didn't pay me anything."

Mr. Holiday couldn't stand the suspense any longer. "Oh Peedie, you didn't take the flowers!"

"Yes, I did," said Peedie. "Mrs. McCree said I'd been such a good helper that she wanted to give me something. So, she handed me this big bunch of flowers. Do you think Mom would like them?"

They all laughed. Then, with the bouquet and the Mother's Day card, they made their way to the kitchen to see Mom.

# Bonus Short Story: See How Uncles Run

"Pow, pow, pow!" Four-year-old Peedie Holiday, eyes squinted and sighting down his drawn and pointed finger, was shooting at his older sister, Nancy, much to her annoyance. When Peedie wasn't glued to the television, he liked to play cowboy.

"Cut that out!" scolded Nancy, who acted Mother when Mother wasn't around.

"I can't. I don't have any scissors." snickered Peedie.

Nancy and Peedie were at Uncle Earl's, while Mom and Dad were attending a funeral. Older brother Jack had stayed with one of his friends. That, by age, put Nancy in charge.

"You better behave, or I'll tell Mom," warned Nancy, to which Peedie made a face. Nancy felt very responsible for Peedie's behavior, especially at Uncle Earls, who was very lax in such things as discipline.

Peedie liked coming to Uncle Earl's because his uncle was a hunter and sportsman. He liked his uncle's knotty-pine den with its mounted deer and the trophies over the fireplace. The room seemed to inspire a recklessness in the normally peaceable Peedie. Nancy sensed his growing wildness and was not certain how much she could rely on her uncle to back up her authority.

Uncle Earl looked in to see how they were doing. "If you kids would like some milk and cookies, they're in the kitchen. Help yourself. I'll be down in the basement tying flies, if you need me.

"Tying flies?" said Peedie, picturing his uncle capturing and roping flies like one of his cowboy heroes. "How do you tie flies?"

"Very carefully," laughed Uncle Earl. "All joking aside, flies are fishing hooks used in fly-casting. I'll show you one later. In the meantime, make yourselves at home."

A mischievous look came over Peedie's face as Uncle Earl left the room and went down to the cellar. Nancy was quick to notice it, and felt called upon to be on guard. She resented having to look after her little brother. She would have preferred doing anything else. Still, she felt it was her duty.

The first thing Peedie did was spy an archery set on a wall rack behind the couch. He quickly climbed up on the tan leather couch to get a closer look at it.

"Peedie! Get down from there! You're not to stand on the furniture," said Nancy, frowning her disapproval.

Reluctantly, Peedie obeyed, but not without a defiant hop, bounce, and jump getting down.

"And don't *jump* on the furniture!"

"Uncle Earl doesn't care," pouted Peedie.

"He does, too," said Nancy, "and I'll tell on you if you don't stop messing around."

For a few minutes, Peedie was quieted. And Nancy looked around the room for something to do. She looked into some of the magazines on the coffee table, but they were all on hunting and fishing and didn't interest her much. She did like the colorful pictures of animals, but not the hunting part. It was while peeking through a stack of magazines that the pile slid and upset a dish of salted peanuts. Some peanut crumbs landed on the floor.

"Humph!" mocked Peedie. "Now who's messing around?"

"Oh, shush. Just don't step on 'em. I'll get a broom."

Seconds later, after finding a broom in the kitchen, Nancy returned to the den. "Peedie, what are you doing?"

Peedie had gotten into a closet and found a shotgun and was holding it.

"Hand me that," said Nancy, "and stop getting into things, or I'll really get angry."

Later, Uncle Earl called them down to his basement workshop to see the fly he was tying. Clamped in a small metal vice was a fishing hook wrapped and knotted around and around with black and yellow thread, to which a feather was fastened.

"Why would the fish eat that?" asked Peedie, wrinkling his nose. "It doesn't look like it'd taste very good."

"It's all in the action of fly casting, Peedie," explained Uncle Earl. "How do you like it, Nancy?"

"The colors are pretty," said Nancy, "although I'd choose different ones."

"Someday, I'll show both of you how to fish with these. Would you like that?"

Not another word was said.

Both Nancy and Uncle Earl turned to see what had happened to Peedie. He had slipped away without their notice and while they were closely examining the fly.

"Where do you suppose he disappeared to?"

Nancy got a pale look on her face.

"Quick, Uncle Earl, up to your den! Peedie found one of your shotguns in a cupboard!"

"Oh, my gosh! And it's loaded, too!" exclaimed Uncle Earl, who took the lead dashing up the stairs.

When they rushed into the den, Peedie sure enough had the shotgun, knowing full well he was doing wrong.

"I won't hurt it," he blurted out. "I just wanted to see it. It's just like the ones cowboys carry on stagecoaches."

"Careful! Watch out how you point that," said Uncle Earl, slowly approaching Peedie.

"It's all right," said Nancy. "I took the shells out of it."

Uncle Earl took the 12-gauge shotgun and looked in the breach of it. "Whew," he said. "You're right. It's not loaded."

"I put the shells on the top shelf," said Nancy.

"Good for you, Nancy. I'm not used to children in the house. But even so, I should be more careful with guns."

Peedie was about to burst into tears.

"That's okay, Peedie. It's all right to be curious. Only when it's something dangerous like guns, ask someone to show you first."

Everyone was all smiles when Mr. and Mrs. Holiday came to get Nancy and Peedie. Uncle Earl was particularly proud of Nancy, and gave her an extra squeeze and hug.

"Don't forget, Nancy. I'm taking you fishing one day soon."

# About the Author

**Edward McClenathan** began his career as a grade school teacher at Fredonia, New York's Wheelock School. Here, he established himself as the school's librarian, welcoming several students of varying grades throughout the day. These students would anxiously await the next story read to them by Mr. McClenathan during their library period, and would also enjoy the accompanying illustrations that he'd draw on chalkboards or overhead projectors.

The author would often choose classics to share with his engaged listeners, but occasionally took the opportunity to introduce them to his own works as well. **"Holidays and Hoopla"** was one such work. Designed to follow a familiar school-year calendar, the chapters weave their way from season to season and holiday to holiday.

These students, now adults, frequently comment to their former librarian that that experience made a big impression on them as a most pleasant early childhood memory. The author wishes this experience on future generations as well.

**Edward McClenathan** studied art at Carnegie Mellon and holds several degrees in Elementary Education, Speech, and Library Science from the State University of New York at Fredonia and the University of Buffalo.


Other Edacious Reader Books™ include:

**"Cat vs. Dog"** (currently available on Amazon)
**"The Verity Scanner"** (coming soon)
**"Oh, Hennery!"** (Peck's Bad Boy) soon to be available as a play or musical.
**ATO** ["Adjusted Traditional Orthography"] A phonetic-learning-to-read and spell alphabet.

# Holidays and Hoopla